FOLGER'S CHOICE: FAVORITES ON OUR FIFTY-FIFTH ANNIVERSARY

The Folger Shakespeare Library

April 10–August 15, 1987

Supported by a grant from
The Chisholm Foundation
in honor of Alexander F. Chisholm.

FOLGER'S CHOICE:
FAVORITES ON
OUR FIFTY-FIFTH
ANNIVERSARY

Copyright 1987.
The Folger Shakespeare Library.

Exhibition hours: daily, 10:00 a.m.–4:00 p.m.

Information: (202) 544-7077.

The Folger Shakespeare Library
201 East Capitol Street, S.E.
Washington, D.C. 20003-1094

The images on the front and back covers are details of objects in the exhibition. Front, left to right: Flemish Allegorical Tapestry (see description no. 55), Biblia Germanica (22), *Ein wahres Probiertes und Pracktisches geschriebenen Feuerbuch* (38). Back, left to right: Esther Inglis, *Octonaries upon the vanity and inconstancy of the world* (34); William Shakespeare, *Songs and Sonnets by Shakespeare* (45); Abraham Ortelius, *The theatre of the whole world* . . . (35).

FOREWORD

This catalogue and the exhibition it records commemorate and celebrate the fifty-fifth anniversary of the Folger Shakespeare Library. When the Library opened officially, on April 23, 1932, in the presence of President Hoover, it was universally recognized as the world's preeminent repository of materials concerning Shakespeare's life, his poems and plays, and the origins, history, and influence of the Elizabethan stage. No one, however, could at that moment have predicted that in addition to enhancing those strengths the Folger would become one of the world's leading centers for research in the continental Renaissance and early modern European literature and history. That a library designed as a memorial to a single, albeit transcendent, author has come to play such an enlarged role follows directly from the expansion of its book and manuscript holdings.

"Folger's Choice" is designed to provide some sense of the range and scope of the collections. It does so, however, in an unsystematic and perhaps even idiosyncratic way. Because this show marks a milestone in the Library's history, we decided to focus attention on fifty-five works that make significant points about the *kind* of "treasure house" the Folger has become. Rather than offer a unified view of this vast terrain, as seen through the eye of a single curator, we have chosen to approach it through a team effort.

Five members of the staff who volunteered their services were each assigned the task of selecting eleven items. Each contributor understood that he or she had absolute freedom either to follow a coherent strand of interest, or to range widely and without any thematic focus. The objective was to refract the Folger's collections from a number of different angles, to approach it from differing points of entry, and to consider and discuss some of its highlights in personal as well as scholarly terms. In so doing, we hope to compensate for a certain unaccustomed lack of linear coherence by introducing greater variety and individuality into a Folger exhibition.

Our five curators made their choices as individuals. From that point on, their work was collaborative. The group met frequently to review selections, critique one another's essays, and consider the many issues posed by the wide array of books, manuscripts, and other works presented here. An extraordinarily congenial and collegial spirit pervaded these meetings. The result therefore embodies individual choices and tastes while representing a consensus amongst colleagues of varied backgrounds and interests.

For me it was a special pleasure to work with these thoughtful and imaginative colleagues. Elizabeth Walsh, Reading Room Supervisor, sees rare books as a means of gaining access to a deeper understanding of their authors and owners. Hence, her selections tend to emphasize revelations of personality and style. The letters by Queen Elizabeth and John Donne are instances of this kind of focus. Janet Alexander Griffin, Director of Museum and Public Programs, selected works that suggest the breadth of the Folger collection—books that reveal the integration of the creative arts and technical sciences, elements that our culture regards as separate, or even incompatible; books that exemplify important stages in the history of printing and illustrating; and items that demonstrate the idea that art inspires art, represented here by Shakespeare's creative legacy. Rosalind Larry, Assistant Reading Room Supervisor, offers her "all time favorites," based on ten years experience in making rare books available to readers. Among her choices are several magnificent fore-edge bindings, handwriting manuals, and some remarkable illustrated volumes on topics ranging from court pageantry to fire fighting. Head Conservator J. Franklin Mowery naturally approaches books and manuscripts above all as artifacts. His special expertise mandated the choice of some of the Folger's rare and elegant bindings including examples in silver, embroidery, and even hairy deerhide. Since he is also responsible for the preservation of all of the Library's holdings, he has included a manuscript and a notable tapestry. My own selections are those of a cultural historian. They give some sense of how fully the literary and intellectual patrimony of Renaissance Europe, from Petrarch and Boccaccio to Montaigne and Cervantes, is present in this place.

As usual, several members of the Folger's staff made notable contributions to this exhibition. As chairman of the exhibition committee, Elizabeth Walsh needed, and possessed, more than the normal degree of patience and humor. The Department of Museum and Public Programs, directed by Janet Alexander Griffin, coordinated the exhibit planning and production—Jenifer Blakemore coordinated the catalogue and graphics and Ann Greer managed the publicity. J. Franklin Mowery, in consultation with Clifford LaFontaine and assisted by Julia Kampelman, restored and installed items in the exhibition. Julie Ainsworth, the Library's tireless photographer, provided the illustrations for the catalogue, with help from Ann Muchoney.

Above all, it is my pleasure to thank the trustees of The Chisholm Foundation of Laurel, Mississippi, for their generous support of this anniversary exhibition and catalogue. The Foundation bears the name of Alexander Field Chisholm (Amherst, '23), whose love of Shakespeare and of literature place him squarely in the tradition of Henry Clay Folger of the Class of 1879. In celebrating the founding of this Library, we also honor the memory of Alexander Chisholm, who appreciated it and handed that appreciation down to a new generation of his family.

Werner Gundersheimer, Director

1

JOHN MILTON

Areopagitica: a speech of Mr. John Milton for the liberty of unlicenc'd printing

London, 1644

John Milton, author of the epic poem *Paradise Lost*, was an early advocate for freedom of the press. This discourse, which was unlicensed and unregistered, was inspired partly by Parliament's attempt to suppress Milton's pamphlet *The Doctrine of Divorce* published in 1643. The title derives from an earlier unspoken speech addressed to the Areopagus, the highest judicial court of ancient Athens by the Athenian orator Isocrates, who was protesting the infringement of liberty. Milton holds that reading, constant testing, and a diversity of opinion are necessary to the growth of virtue and knowledge. "Truth is stronger than falsehood," he concludes, and "gross conforming stupidity is more to be feared than new opinions." ***EW***

AREOPAGITICA;

A SPEECH

OF

Mr. JOHN MILTON

For the Liberty of Vnlicenc'd PRINTING,

To the Parlament of England.

Τοὐλεύθερον δ' ἐκεῖνο, εἴ τις θέλει πόλει
Χρηστόν τι βούλευμ' εἰς μέσον φέρειν, ἔχων.
Καὶ ταῦθ' ὁ χρῄζων, λαμπρός ἐσθ', ὁ μὴ θέλων,
Σιγᾷ. τί τούτων ἔστ' ἰσαίτερον πόλει;

Euripid. Hicetid.

This is true Liberty when free born men
Having to advise the public may speak free,
Which he who can, and will, deserv's high praise,
Who neither can nor will, may hold his peace;
What can be juster in a State then this?

Euripid. Hicetid.

LONDON,
Printed in the Yeare, 1644.

2

Kalendrier des bergers

[London, Thomas Este, 1570?]

This almanac, known as the Shepherd's Calendar, enjoyed wide popularity through several centuries following its first printing at Paris in 1493. The first satisfactory translation into English was done by Richard Copeland about 1518 and it became the standard text for subsequent English editions.

The calendar is divided into five sections. Part one contains astronomical and ecclesiastical data, including charts for determining the signs of the zodiac and lunar eclipses, as well as tables for calculating the date of Easter and other moveable religious feasts.

Concerned with man's spiritual health, parts two and three are a study of the seven deadly sins and the seven cardinal virtues. The fourth part offers medical advice based on the effect of the planets on various parts of the body and offers treatments for a variety of common complaints. Part five is a cosmology which tries to explain man in terms of the universe in which he lives and the effect of the planets on human personality. Also included are the general characteristics of individuals born under each of the signs of the zodiac—the same sort of information which continues to have mass popular appeal even to the present day. ***EW***

The Shepardes Kalender.

HERE BEGINNETH THE KALENDER OF
Shepardes Newly Augmented, and Corrected.

WILLIAM SHAKESPEARE

Mr. William Shakespeares comedies, histories and tragedies

London, Isaac Jaggard and Ed. Blount, 1623

Seven years after the death of William Shakespeare this volume of his collected works was published. Compiled and edited by two of his fellow actors, John Heminges and Henry Condell, the First Folio, as the book is called, contained thirty-six of Shakespeare's plays, eighteen of which had never before been printed. Among the plays first printed in the Folio are *Macbeth, The Tempest,* and *As You Like It.* On the title page of this volume is the now famous portrait of Shakespeare engraved by Martin Droeshout. This portrait is one of only two authentic likenesses of the author, the other being the bust over Shakespeare's tomb at Trinity Church in Stratford-upon-Avon. Of the approximately 1,000 copies of this volume printed, only about 240 can be accounted for today. The Folger Library collection includes seventy-nine copies of the First Folio, all of which were acquired by Henry Clay Folger.
EW

To the Reader.

This Figure, that thou here seest put,
  It was for gentle Shakespeare cut;
Wherein the Grauer had a strife
  with Nature, to out-doo the life :
O, could he but haue drawne his wit
  As well in brasse, as he hath hit
His face ; the Print would then surpasse
  All, that vvas euer vvrit in brasse.
But, since he cannot, Reader, looke
  Not on his Picture, but his Booke.

                    B. I.

Mr. WILLIAM SHAKESPEARES

COMEDIES, HISTORIES, & TRAGEDIES.

Published according to the True Originall Copies.

Martin Droeshout sculpsit London.

LONDON
Printed by Isaac Iaggard, and Ed. Blount. 1623.

4

WILLIAM SHAKESPEARE

Mr. William Shakespeares comedies, histories and tragedies

London, Thos. Cotes, 1632

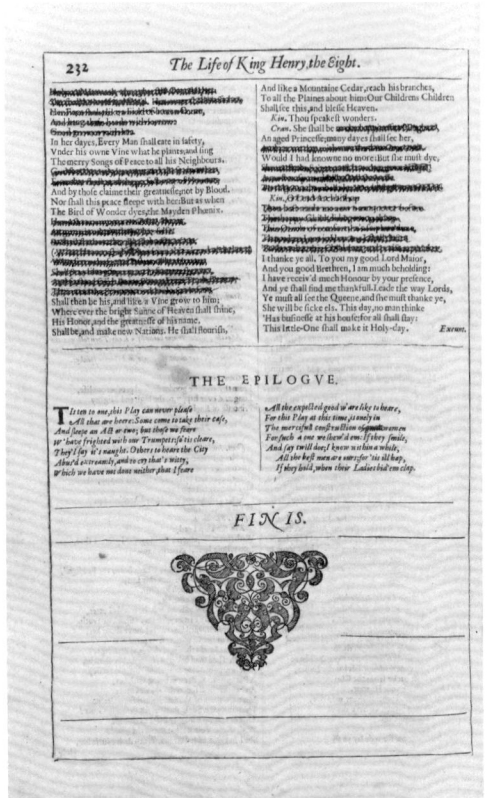

The second edition of Shakespeare's works, or the Second Folio, was printed in the shop of Thomas Cotes who took over the Jaggard print shop after the death of Isaac Jaggard in 1627. It contains all of the plays in the First Folio, but with some textual emendations and corrections. Added to the preliminary poems in praise of the author is John Milton's *An Epitaph on Shakespeare*, thought to be Milton's first published poem. Fifty-seven copies of the Second Folio are in the Folger collection.

A notation on the title page of this volume reads, "This book has been expurgated and approved by authority of the Holy Office by William Sanchez, Society of Jesus." The Holy Office was the ecclesiastical jurisdiction charged with the detection and punishment of all heretics and persons guilty of any offense against Catholic orthodoxy. Books were routinely expurgated by blotting out the offensive passages with printer's ink. Words, phrases, and occasionally whole sections, such as the closing scene from the play *Henry VIII*, fell victim to the pen of the Inquisition.

Extolling the infant princess Elizabeth, Cranmer's praises echo biblical passages and employ images generally used to describe the Virgin Mary. The expurgated lines read in part:

> She must, the saints must have her; yet a virgin
> A most unsported lily shall she pass
> To th' ground and all the world shall mourn her.

EW

Mr. WILLIAM SHAKESPEARES

COMEDIES, HISTORIES, and TRAGEDIES.

Published according to the true Originall Copies.

The second Impression.

Martin Droeshout sculpsit London.

LONDON,
Printed by *Tho. Cotes,* for *Iohn Smethwick,* and are to be sold at his shop
in Saint *Dunstans* Church-yard. 1632.

*Opus auctoritate Sancti officij permissum et expurgatum eadem
authoritate per Guilielmum Sanchaum è Soc.tte Jesu.*

5

WILLIAM SHAKESPEARE

Mr. William Shakespeares comedies, histories and tragedies

London, 1664

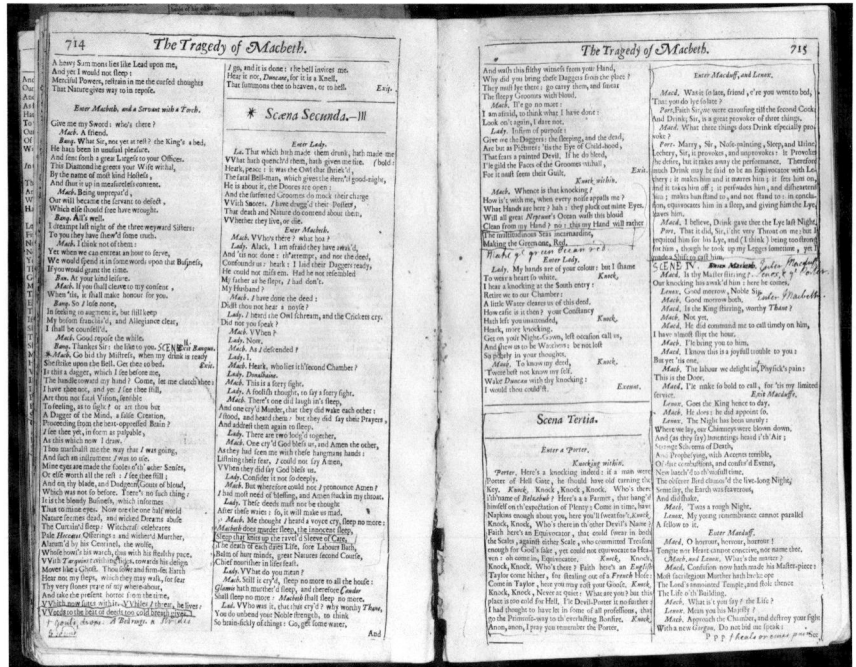

The title page of this third edition of Shakespeare's works, or Third Folio, boasts the addition of seven new plays never before printed. However, only one of these plays, *Pericles,* has been accepted as a Shakespeare work. The Folger collection contains twenty-three copies of the Third Folio.

Considerable evidence suggests that this volume belonged to the 18th-century author Alexander Pope and was used by him in the preparation of his 1725 edition of Shakespeare's works. Pope sought to make Shakespeare more intelligible and instructive for the contemporary reader by rearranging portions of the text, by incorporating lines from earlier published quarto editions of the plays into the folio text, and by removing lines or passages which he thought were inferior. This Folio contains extensive margin notes probably in the hand of Pope. Underlined passages were to be retained, but moved to another place on the page; boxed text was to be deleted. Those passages marked with stars were considered by Pope to be particularly important to the reader. **_EW_**

Mr. WILLIAM SHAKESPEAR'S

Comedies, Histories, and Tragedies.

Published according to the true Original Copies.

The third Impression.

And unto this Impression is added seven Playes, never before Printed in Folio.

viz.

Pericles Prince of *Tyre*.
The *London Prodigall*.
The History of *Thomas* Ld *Cromwell*.
Sir *John Oldcastle* Lord *Cobham*.
The *Puritan Widow*.
A *York-shire* Tragedy.
The Tragedy of *Locrine*.

LONDON, Printed for P. C. 1664.

WILLIAM SHAKESPEARE

Mr. William Shakespeares comedies, histories and tragedies

London, 1685

The fourth edition of Shakespeare's works, or the Fourth Folio, was printed in 1685 and is essentially a reprint of the Third Folio. It contains the additional seven plays that first appeared in the 1664 edition, as well as a good deal of correction and modernization of the text designed to make it easier to read and understand. The library collection includes thirty-six copies of the Fourth Folio.

This copy is the first "rare" item to be acquired by Henry Folger. In 1889 he bought the volume at Bangs auction in New York city for $107.50 to be paid in four installments over a thirty-day period. This purchase was Henry Folger's first venture in the field and marked his serious entry into the area of rare-book collecting. **_EW_**

Mʀ. William Shakespear's COMEDIES, HISTORIES, AND TRAGEDIES.

Published according to the true Original Copies.

Unto which is added, SEVEN PLAYS,

Never before Printed in Folio:

VIZ.

Pericles Prince of Tyre.
The London Prodigal.
The History of Thomas Lord Cromwel.
Sir John Oldcastle Lord Cobham.
The Puritan Widow.
A Yorkshire Tragedy.
The Tragedy of Locrine.

The Fourth Edition.

Thomas Rayner, Brewer at Limehouse, S.ᵗ Ann's Midd

LONDON,

Printed for *H. Herringman, E. Brewster, R. Chiswell,* and *R. Bentley,* at the *Anchor* in the *New Exchange*; and at the *Crane,* and *Rose* and *Crown* in St. *Pauls* Church-Yard, and in *Russel*-Street Covent-Garden. 1 6 8 5.

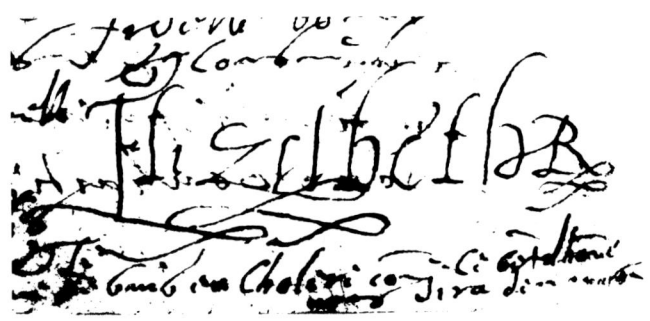

ELIZABETH I

Letter to Henry IV of France

ca. 1595

The assassination of France's King Henry III in August 1589 brought to the throne the Protestant Henry of Navarre as Henry IV, first of the Bourbon kings. At the time France was still suffering the effects of many years of religious strife between the Catholics, represented by the Catholic League, and the Protestants, or Huguenots as they were called. Henry's immediate objectives were to stabilize the situation in France and to secure his throne. Since one of the active supporters of the League was Spain's King Philip II, himself a Catholic, it is not surprising that Henry looked to England's Protestant Queen Elizabeth for advice and support. This letter, written in Elizabeth's own hand, provides insight into the personal side of the Queen as she offers Henry the benefit of her wisdom, not as one sovereign to another but as an older to a younger friend.

> For as to my son if I had one, I would rather see him brave than a coward. You show yourself to have more need of a bridle than a spur. For the honor of God, consider how important to the whole cause is the preservation of your person.... You will forgive me for telling you what would be called bravery in another will be put down to rashness in you and a lack of judgement which is most unbecoming in a great prince.

Having encountered similar religious unrest in her own nation upon her accession to the throne, Elizabeth counseled Henry with the voice of her own experience:

> ... perhaps you will despise this advice coming from a—from the heart of a woman but when you remember how many times I have not shown too much fear in my breast of pistols and swords which have been prepared for me this idea will pass away....

The letter is signed with her elegant signature, Elizabeth R. ***EW***

8

MARCUS TULLIUS CICERO

Commentū familiare in Ciceronis officia

[Lyons, 1502]

Thys boke is myne Prynce Henry

During the Renaissance the study of Latin was fundamental to the education of all schoolboys, including the young prince of Wales who became Henry VIII. Students progressed from basic Latin grammar to a more intensive study and imitation of the classic masters. The most influential of these Roman prose writers was Cicero. In their compositions students were encouraged to aspire to Ciceronian purity of language. Cicero's writings have left their mark on the study of ethics, political thought, ideas of conduct, the development of oratory, letter writing, logic, and rhetoric, and his works are a valuable source of historical information on Roman life and times.

In a large, bold hand the young Henry has written on the first leaf:

"Thys boke is myne Prince Henry."

EW

M.Tullij Ciceronis officioȝ procmiū   Fo. I

Ūanq̄ te Marce fili. In huius pœmij principio ⁊ beniuoluȝ ⁊ attentum reddit filiū suū Cicero.beniuoluȝ qdem:qȝ filiū appellat: attētuȝ v̄o:qȝ docet necessarium esse si negligētie notā vitare velit: phīe incūbere:cuȝ oīa habeat q̄ ad eam auxiliari possint. Pȝceptorem videlȝ optimū:qȝ Cratippum:locū laudatissimum:qȝ gymnasium Atheniēse.Tps oportunū: qȝ iam annū audierit.Fortuna satis vberē cuȝ tā bnficiū habeat pȝes. Rez pterea quā dicat decētissimam: qȝ sapiam moralē eloquētie adiūctaȝ. Monet aūt vt grecis latina piūgat.⟨Co⟩do ē. O Marce fili q̄q̄ opȝ te audietez cratippū: philosophū illū optimuȝ: annū.i.p anni spaciū: ⁊ id athenis.i.in ciuitate atheniēsi:vbi bona docētur ⁊ bn viuitur: abūdare.i.abūdātez ee p̄ceptis.i.regulis ⁊ documētis phīe:ppter summā auctoritatē doctoris tui videlȝ cratippi: qȝ p ⁊ institutis.i.bonis morib⁹ ⁊ cōsuetudinib⁹ riuēdi:ppter auctoritatez vrbis:scȝ athenarum: quoȝ: scȝ doctoris ⁊ vrbis alter videlȝ doctor:cratipp⁹: pōt augere te.i.auctiorem ⁊ copiosiorem efficere: scia.i.in ipsa phīa: ⁊ altera videlȝ vrbis atheniē.in qua gloriose multi vixerūt. pōt augere te exēplis.i.p exēpla bonoȝ viroȝ:tn vt.i.quēadmoduȝ ipse.i.ego. cōiūxi sp latina sup. eloquia ⁊ dogmata cū grecis ad mea vtilitatem:neqȝ.i.⁊ nō feci id.i.nō coniūxi latina cū grecis solum.i.solūmodo in phīa.i.in studio sapie ⁊ in libris de sapia

M.Tullij Ciceronis Officioȝ Liber primus ad Marcum filium.

Uanquā te Marce fili annū iam audientem Cratippū idq̄ Athenis abūdare oportet pceptis institutisq̄ phīe : propter summam ⁊ doctoris auctoritatē ⁊ vrbis quoȝ alter te scientia augere pōt:altera exemplis :tn vt ipse ad meā vtilitatez semp cū grecis latina coniūxi.neqȝ id in philosophia solum: sed etiaȝ in dicēdi exercitatiōe feci: idem tibi cēseo faciedū:vt par sis in vtriusqȝ orōnis facultate. Quā quidem ad rem nos (vt videmur) magnū adiumētuȝ attulimus hoībus nr̄is: vt nō modo grecarum l̄rarum rudes:sȝ etiā docti aliq̄tuȝ se arbitrētur adeptos:⁊ ad dicēduȝ ⁊ ad iudicāduz disquirētibus:sȝ etiā in exercitatione dicēdi.i.in facultate oratoria: ita sup.ego cēseo idem faciēdum sup.esse tibi.i.a te: vt sis par.i.pari formis ⁊ indifferēs atqȝ equaliter abundās in facultate vtriusqȝ orōnis:grece videlȝ ⁊ latine.Ad quā quidez rem.i.ad quā vtriusqȝ orōnis facultatem nos attulimus.i.ego cicero attuli (sed vrbane ⁊ modeste pluraliter loquitur) vt videmur.i.vt ego video: vel mihi vel alijs:hoībus nostris.i.latinis: magnū adiūmētum: vt non modo.i.nō solum rudes.i.ruditer ⁊ vulgariter periti grecaruȝ l̄rarum:sȝ etiā docti arbitrētur se adoptos:aliquātum.i.aliqualiter multuȝ:qd modeste dicit: ⁊.i.simul ad dicēdum dū ipsi eloqui valet:⁊ ad iudicādum de alioȝ:videlȝ locutione: ⁊ scia.hoc est ad phīam:sine qua nemo recte iudicare pōt.Quia opȝ bonū iudicem bene nosse:qd phīa docȝ. ⟨Quanq̄ ⁊.etsi vt docet valla lib.ij.sequētis orōnis dignitatem quādaȝ ipse ferūt:voluūtqȝ quoties in principio orōnis ponitur ꝗbuȝ indicatiui modi: qn vero scdo loco: etiā subiūctiū.hoc ergo loco rem magnaȝ aggressus bene dixit:q̄q̄ opȝ. ⟨Annus ab an qd circū est deductū videtur.Est eīm solis circuuolutio a quouis pūcto in idipm.vn a primis mortalibus ante inuētas l̄ras dracōne caudaȝ suam mordēre significabatur.hinc maro in Geo:g. In se sua p vestigia voluitur annus.Quod aūt acto vtitur bm Seruiū ad venustiorem locutiōem ptinet: ⁊ bm nonlū marcellū ad ꝯtinua tionem tpis.Naȝ quoties inquit per acttm annos vel dies loqmur iuges.i.cōtinuos anosvel dies vocamus:quoties per ablm̄ interiectis aliquibus annis vel diebus. Sed valla vtruncqȝ irridet docēs per actm more greco potius q̄ latino ⁊ sine cōtinuatione tpis loqui posse. Idez nestor asserit.Si tn perissimor exēpla intueri voluerimus:tam seruius q̄ marcellū recte locutum dixerimus.Ratio eīm vbi cōtinuus est tps q̄diu seu q̄dudum quid fit aut factū aut futurum est:aliter q̄ in acto locuti sunt.licet notā ꝯtinuationis aliq̄i adiecerint:sicut totos dies ⁊ integros annos.Unde in sexto Eneidos. Propter continuationez temporis dicitur. Noctes atqȝ dies patatri ianua ditis. Quod si intercapedo esset diceret.noctibus atqȝ diebus. Possumus tamen tempus cōtinuatum sicut quodlibet,in quo aliquit fit in ablatiuo ponere:vt vigi

9

JOHN DONNE
Letter to Sir George More
March 1602

Just before Christmas in 1601, poet John Donne secretly married Anne More, daughter of Sir George More of Loseley Hall. Marrying a girl without her father's permission, he committed offenses against both the civil and Canon Laws. For these infractions, and at the insistence of his new father-in-law, Donne found himself in Fleet prison and banned from all communication with his bride. Donne responded with a series of letters to Sir George More attempting to explain his motives and begging for mercy. He wrote:

> I therefore humbly beseech you to have so charitable pity of what I have and do and must suffer as to take you to yourself in the comfort of having saved from such destruction as your just anger might have laid upon him a sorrowful and honest man.

Donne's appeals were eventually heeded, and on the 27th of April, the court of the Archbishop of Canterbury confirmed the marriage of John and Anne Donne. Despite some years of financial difficulties caused by the scandal surrounding their marriage, the Donnes appear to have enjoyed a happy and productive married life. When Anne Donne died in 1617, the inscription over her tomb reports that she was survived by her husband and seven children. ***EW***

Sr

If I could fear, yt in so much worthynes as ys in yrs there wer no mercy, or yf these waights opprest onely my shoulders, and my fortunes, and not my conscience, and hers whose good ys dearer to me by much then my lyfe, I should not thus troble yrs wth my Lrs. But when I see that this storme hath shakd me at roote, in my Lords favor, wher I was well planted, and have iust reason to fear, that those yll reports wch malice hath raysd of me may have trobled her, I can leave no honest way vntryed to remedy these miseryes, nor find any way more honest then this, owt of an humble and repentant hart, for the fault donne to yrs to beg both yr pardon and assistance in my suite to my L. I should wrong yrs as much agayne as I did, if I should think yrs sought to destroy me. but though I be not hedlongly destroyd, I languish and rust dangerously. from seeking preferments abrode, my love and conscience restraines me. from hoping for them here my Lords disgracings cut me of. My Emprisonmts and theyrs whose love to me brought them to yt hath already cost me 40l. And the love of my frinds, though yt be not utterly grownded vpon my fortunes, yet I know suffers somewhat in these long and vncertain disgraces of myne. I therfore humbly beseech yrs to have so charitable a pitty, of what I have, and do, and must suffer as to take to yr selfe the comfort, of having saved from such destruction as yr iust anger might have layd vpon him a sorowfull and honest man. I was bold in my last letter to beg leave of yrs that I might wright to yr daughter. Though I vnderstood thervpon, that after the Thursday yrs were not displeased that I should, yet I have not nor wyll not wthowt yr knowledge do yt. But now I beseech yrs that I may; since I protest before god, yt is the greatest of my afflictions, not to do yt. In all the world ys not more true sorrow then in my hart, nor more vnderstanding of true repentance then in yrs. And therfore God, whose pardon in such cases ys never denyed, gives me leave to hope, that yrs wyll favorably consider my necessityes. To his mercifull guiding, and protection I comend yrs and cease to troble yrs. 1° Mart: 1601

yrs in all humblenes
and dutifull obedience

J: Donne

Incipiunt hore beate marie virginis secudum usum sarum

Paris, [Philippe Pigouchet], 1497

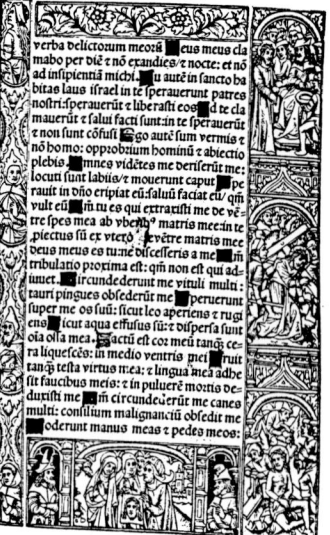

The Book of Hours was not an official church service book but was designed for private devotions and contained prayers to be recited at the canonical hours. It was not uncommon to find a Book of Hours in homes which had no other books. All editions had a calendar of fixed religious festivals at the beginning, followed by an almanac giving the date of Easter for a range of years. The hours of the Virgin were often interspersed with verses and responses which varied with the local customs. These variations are called the "use" and are often defined by the region in which they occur. The Sarum or the Salisbury use was the most common in England.

This Book of Hours of the Salisbury use is printed on vellum with hand-colored illuminated letters throughout the text. Many of the devotions are illustrated with intricate woodcuts. One leaf of the volume bears the inscription:

> Madam I pray
> You Remember
> me in your god
> prayers your
> mastras
>   Elizabeth R

in the hand of Elizabeth of York, mother of King Henry VIII. *EW*

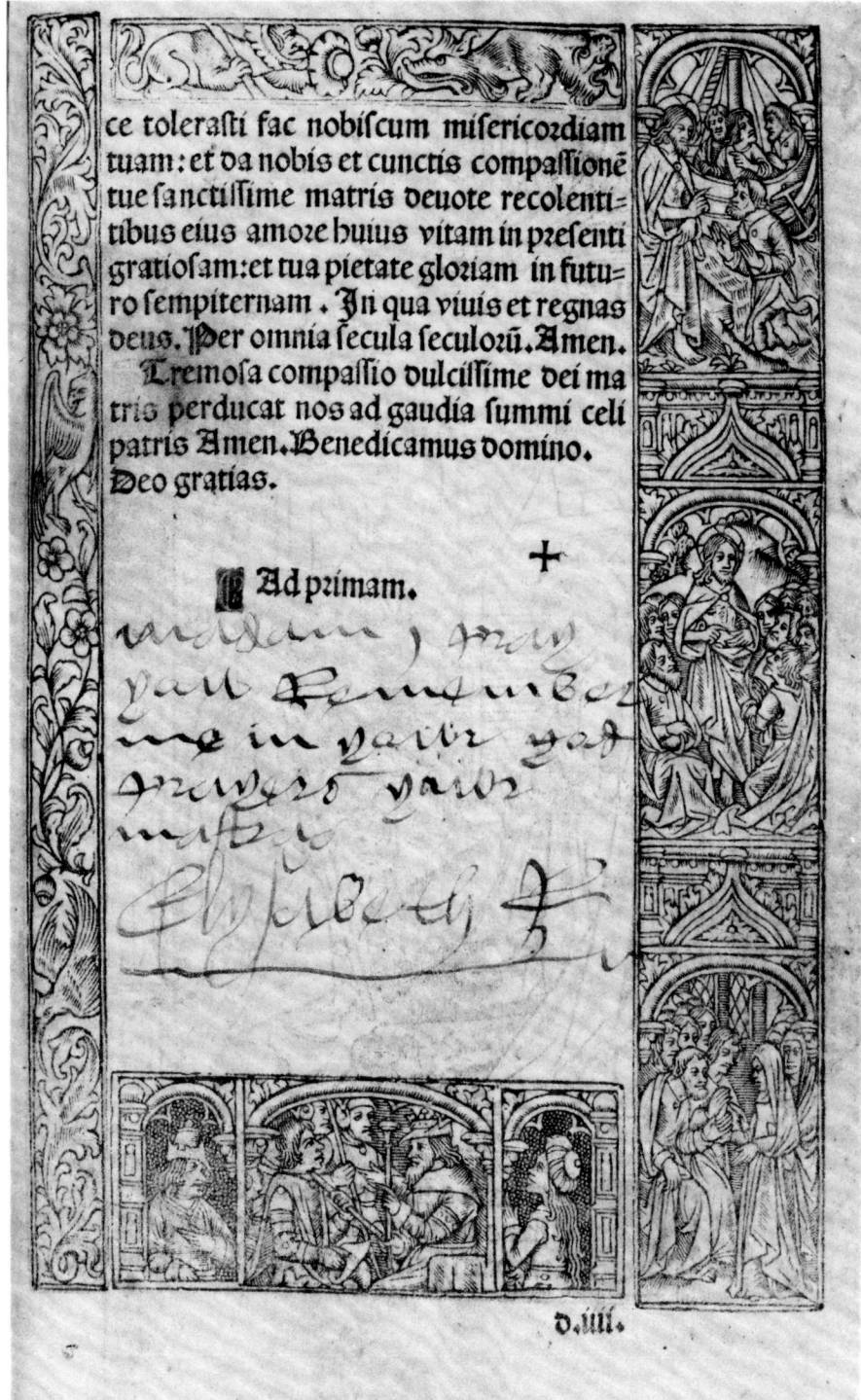

ce tolerasti fac nobiscum misericordiam tuam: et da nobis et cunctis compassionē tue sanctissime matris deuote recolentitibus eius amore huius vitam in presenti gratiosam: et tua pietate gloriam in futuro sempiternam. In qua viuis et regnas deus. Per omnia secula seculorū. Amen.

Lremosa compassio dulcissime dei matris perducat nos ad gaudia summi celi patris Amen. Benedicamus domino. Deo gratias.

¶ Ad primam.

madam I pray yow remember me in yowr goode prayers mastres Elizabeth

EDWARD TOPSELL

The Historie of Foore-Footed Beastes

London, William Iaggard, 1607

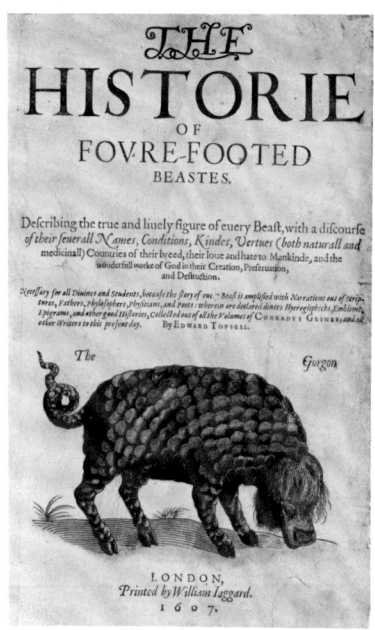

English clergyman Edward Topsell's chief claim to fame was as the compiler of two elaborate manuals of zoology, *The Historie of Foore-Footed Beastes* and *The Historie of Serpents* (1608). His texts and illustrations were based largely on the work of German naturalist Konrad Gesner, whose *Historiae Animalium* had been printed in 1585. To Gesner's basic text Topsell added exhaustive accounts of the prevailing traditions and scientific beliefs of his own age that give his works their own historical value. The book is a charming combination of heresay evidence intermixed with historical fact— a combination common in the Renaissance. The animals included in this history range from the dog, cow, and horse to the more exotic gorgon and sphinx. Each illustration is accompanied by elaborate descriptions of the creature, gleaned either from early literature or actual contemporary sightings. The book also provides interesting and useful facts about each animal. For example, Topsell praises the strength and endurance of the camel and notes that its milk has been found to be an antidote against poison and to ease shortness of breath. Topsell recommends drinking dried brain of a camel mixed with vinegar as a cure for the falling sickness.
EW

Of the Cammell.

Morus.
Maulbeerbaum.

INTRINSECVS.

Qualemcumq; stomachum Mora celsi, ut uocant, offenderint, talem saa
ne relinquunt. Si namq; is bene se habuerit hisce nihil læditur, sin uero ali
ter, facile in illo corrumpentur Mora.   Inflam

HIERONYMUS BOCK

Hieronymi Tragi, De Stirpium. . . .

Argentorati, Wendelinus Rihelius, 1552

While Thisbe is "tarrying in mulberry shade," the unfortunate Pyramus, thinking that his lady love has been eaten by a lion, draws the "bloody, blameful blade" and stabs himself. Thus is Ovid's tale retold by Shakespeare in *A Midsummer Night's Dream* (1600), but depicted here half a century earlier by David Kandel, illustrator of Hieronymus Bock's great botanical work.

During his career Bock was a student of medicine, a schoolmaster, a Lutheran minister, as well as Count Palatine Ludwig's superintendant of gardens. His greatest achievement, however, was in descriptive botany, as Bock was one of the first great herbalists to make detailed notes on all stages of plant life rather than concentrating as his predecessors had on the flowering stage. There were at least a dozen editions of this popular herbal, including this Latin translation of the original German, *Kreuter Buch* (1546). ***JAG***

DENIS DIDEROT, ED.

Encyclopédie

Paris, Briasson, 1751-65

A monumental figure of the Enlightenment, Denis Diderot (1713-1784) changed the intellectual history of Europe as editor of the *Encyclopédie*. Now a common research tool for all students, the encyclopedia was a brave new concept when the publication of this great work was first announced in 1750. The idea that all forms of thought, from philosophy to techniques of making candles, were interrelated and appropriate for study by all men was quite new. The *Encyclopédie* proved to be a brave, revolutionary publication, not only because it provided all readers with compact instruction for technical advancement, but also because its political tracts by Voltaire, Rousseau, and others propounded a new, secular ideology of progress. This liberalism strengthened a growing interest of the middle classes in improving their station in this world, rather than merely enduring this world until the next was attained. The *Encyclopédie*, a mammoth set of some thirty volumes in all, occupying two shelves in the Folger, was a recognizable step toward the ensuing French Revolution.

JAG

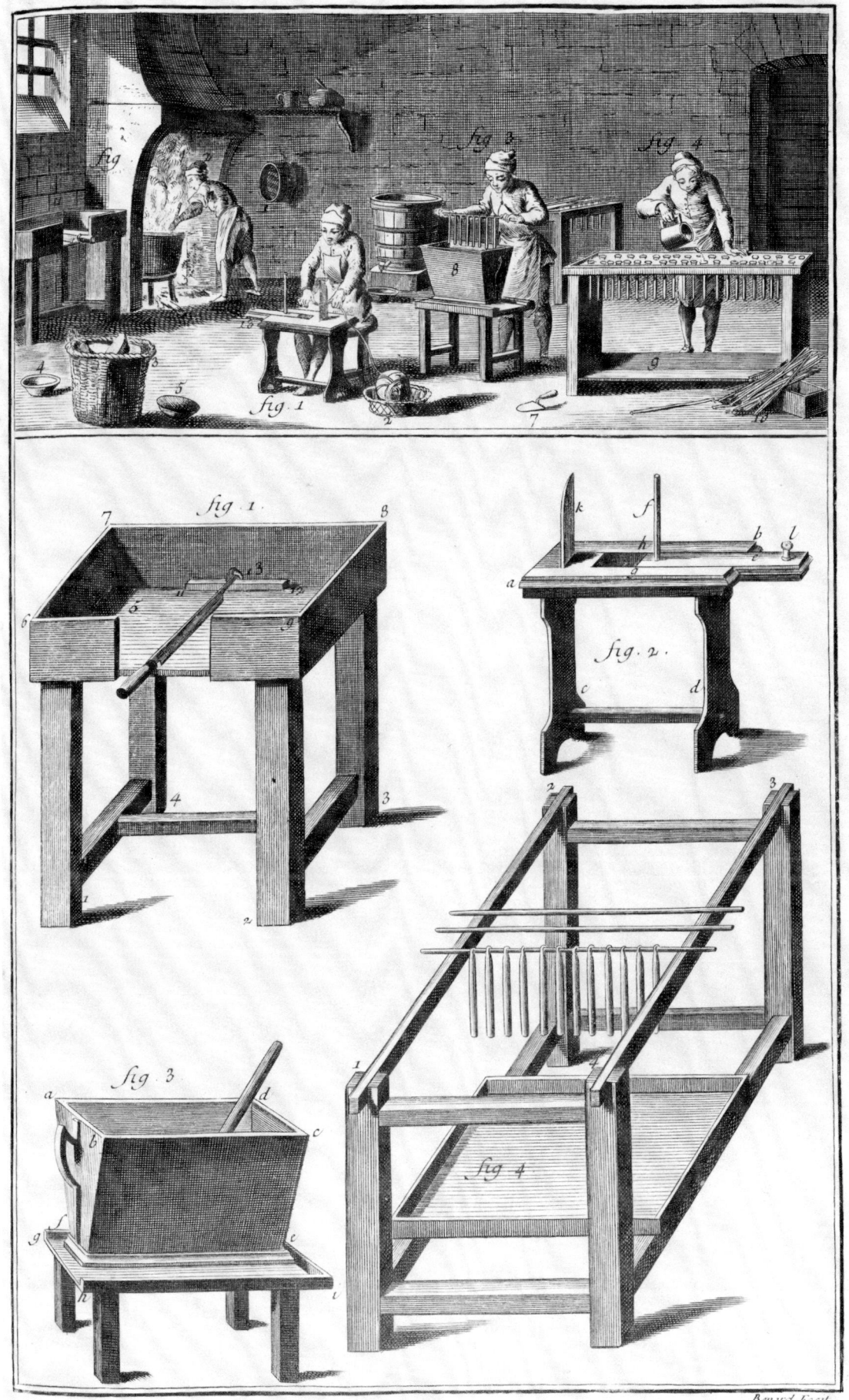

Chandelier.

ANDREA PALLADIO
I quattro libri dell'architetture....
Venetia, Bartolomeo Carampello, 1581

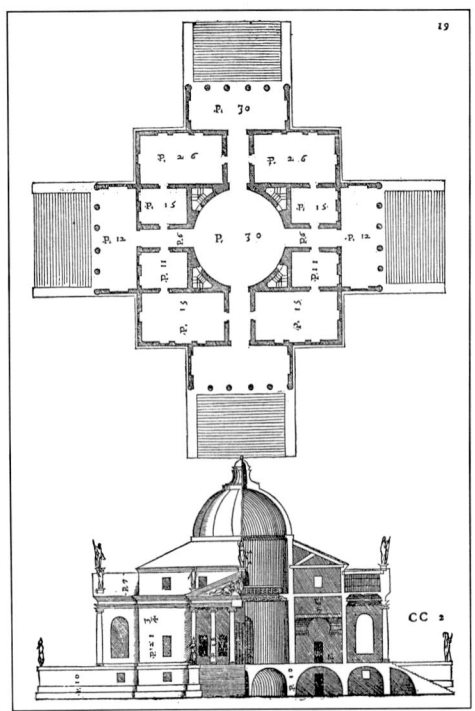

The work of the Italian Andrea Palladio (1508-1580), famous for its elegant harmony of parts and strong symmetry, is thought to have been imitated more than any other architecture in history. Particularly in England and America, successive generations of architects have turned to what is now known as a "classical" style, using elements which Palladio discovered and adapted in his study of the ruins of ancient Greece and Rome. Buildings all over Washington, including the Supreme Court and the Jefferson Memorial, are reminiscent of Palladian style. One of the more famous proponents of Palladio's architecture in America was Thomas Jefferson, who modeled the University of Virginia on Palladio's Villa Meledo.

The *Quattro Libri* was a practical book, written for practicing architects, with specific information on building materials and construction methods. It has been translated and reprinted for centuries since its first publication in 1570, and perhaps had its most profound impact in London, where it served as a guide in the rebuilding of London after the Great Fire of 1666. ***JAG***

60   LIBRO

LA SEGVENTE fabrica fù cominciata dal Conte Francesco, e Conte Lodouico fratelli de' Trissini, à Meledo Villa del Vicentino. Il sito è bellissimo: percioche è sopra uno colle, il quale è bagnato da vn piaceuole fiumicello, & è nel mezo di vna multo spaciosa pianura, & à canto ha vna assai frequente strada. Nella sommità del colle ha da esserui la Sala ritonda, circondata dalle stanze, e però tanto alta che pigli il lume sopra di quelle. Sono nella Sala alcune meze colonne, che tolgono suso un poggiuolo, nel quale si entra per le stanze di sopra; lequali perche sono alte solo sette piedi; seruono per mezati. Sotto il piano delle prime stanze ui sono le cucine, i tinelli, & altri luoghi. Et perche ciascuna faccia ha bellissime uiste; uiuanno quattro loggie di ordine Corinthio: sopra i frontespicii delle quali sorge la cupola della Sala. Le loggie, che tendono alla circonferenza fanno vn gratissimo aspetto, più presso al piano sono i fenili, le cantine, le stalle, i granari, i luoghi da Gastaldo, & altre stanze per vso di Villa; le colonne di questi portici sono di ordine Toscano; sopra il fiume ne gli angoli del cortile vi sono due colombare.

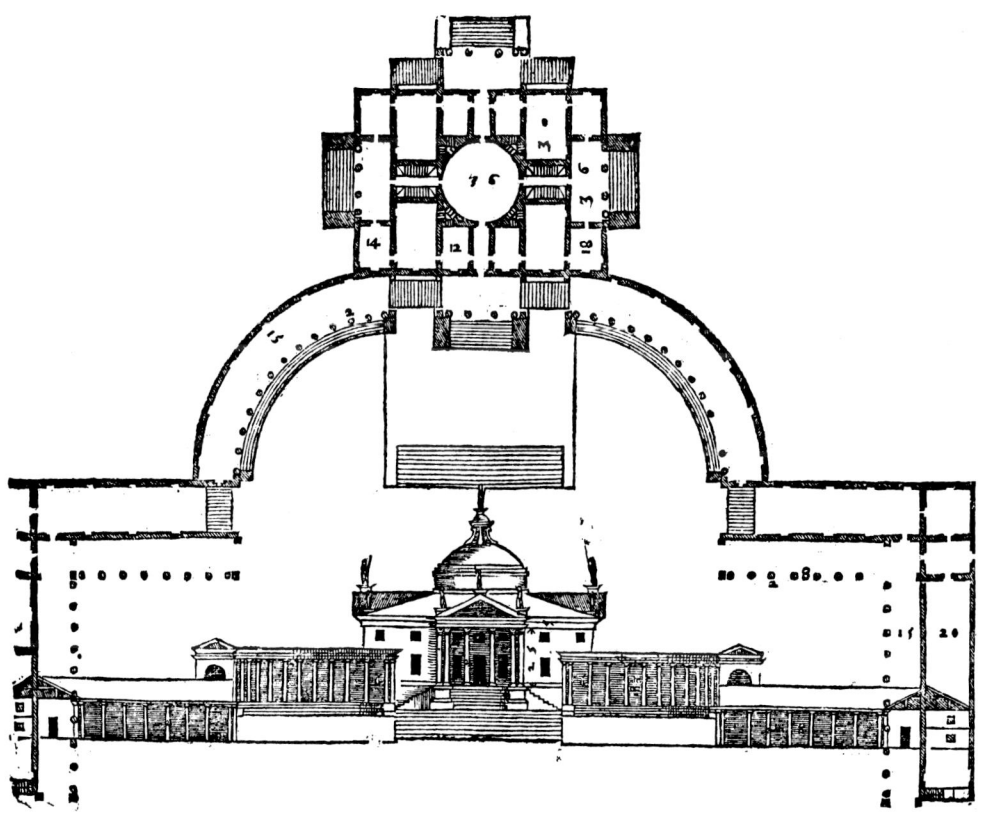

LA FABRICA

JOHANN REMMELIN
Catoptrum Microcosmicum....

Frankfurt am Main, Anton Hummen, 1660

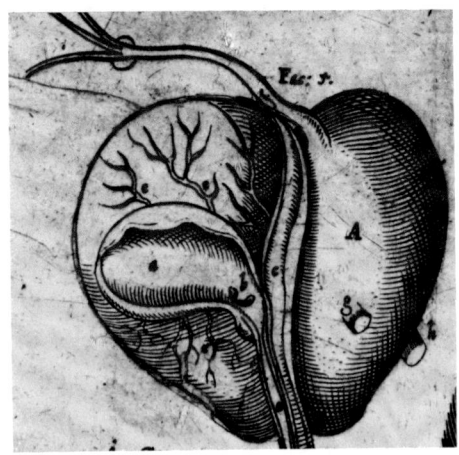

The art of depicting aspects of the anatomy on connected and successive overlays of paper reached its height in the work of Johann Remmelin, who first published this "pop-up" anatomical atlas in 1613. With up to twenty superimposed layers, Remmelin reveals internal organs, bones, the circulatory system, and so forth, while also offering elaborate drapes and allegorical allusions to the many parts of the body. This elaborate graphic dissection had immediate effects on medical instruction and reflects the considerable advances in the understanding of the body that took place in the Renaissance. Needless to say, the volume's three large copperplate engravings with approximately 120 flaps were a printer's nightmare. Nevertheless, Remmelin's work was issued in a number of editions, some of which were painstakingly hand-colored on all levels. ***JAG***

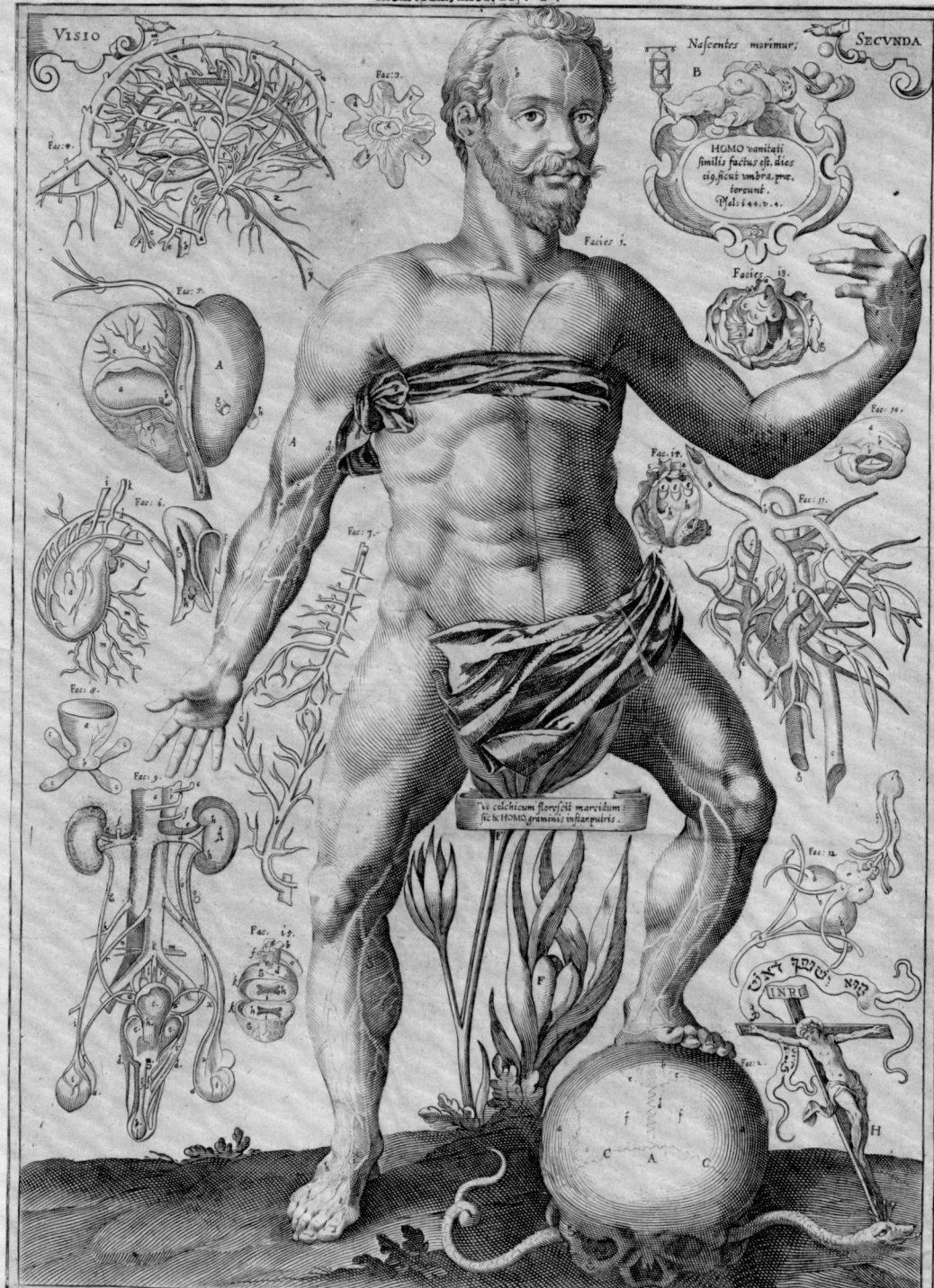

CLAES JANSZ VISSCHER

Londinum Florentissma Britanniae Urbs

[ca. 1625]

The Amsterdam engraver Visscher provides a panoramic view of London before the Great Fire of 1666. Many landmarks can be recognized on both sides of the heavily traveled Thames—St. Paul's, London Bridge, Southwark Cathedral, and the Globe playhouse. Visscher depicts the Globe as polygonal, rather than simply round, as some scholars argue it was and as Hollar later showed it. However, Visscher's theatre may have been the original Globe which burned to the ground in 1613 after an all-too-realistic prop, a cannon, ignited the roof during a performance of *Henry VIII*. Pointing to other inaccuracies, some suggest that Visscher may not have ever visited London, but relied on other available maps and views. This beautiful engraving, the first version of which was issued in 1616, the year of Shakespeare's death, is nonetheless an exciting portrait of the bustling London as Shakespeare must have known it. ***JAG***

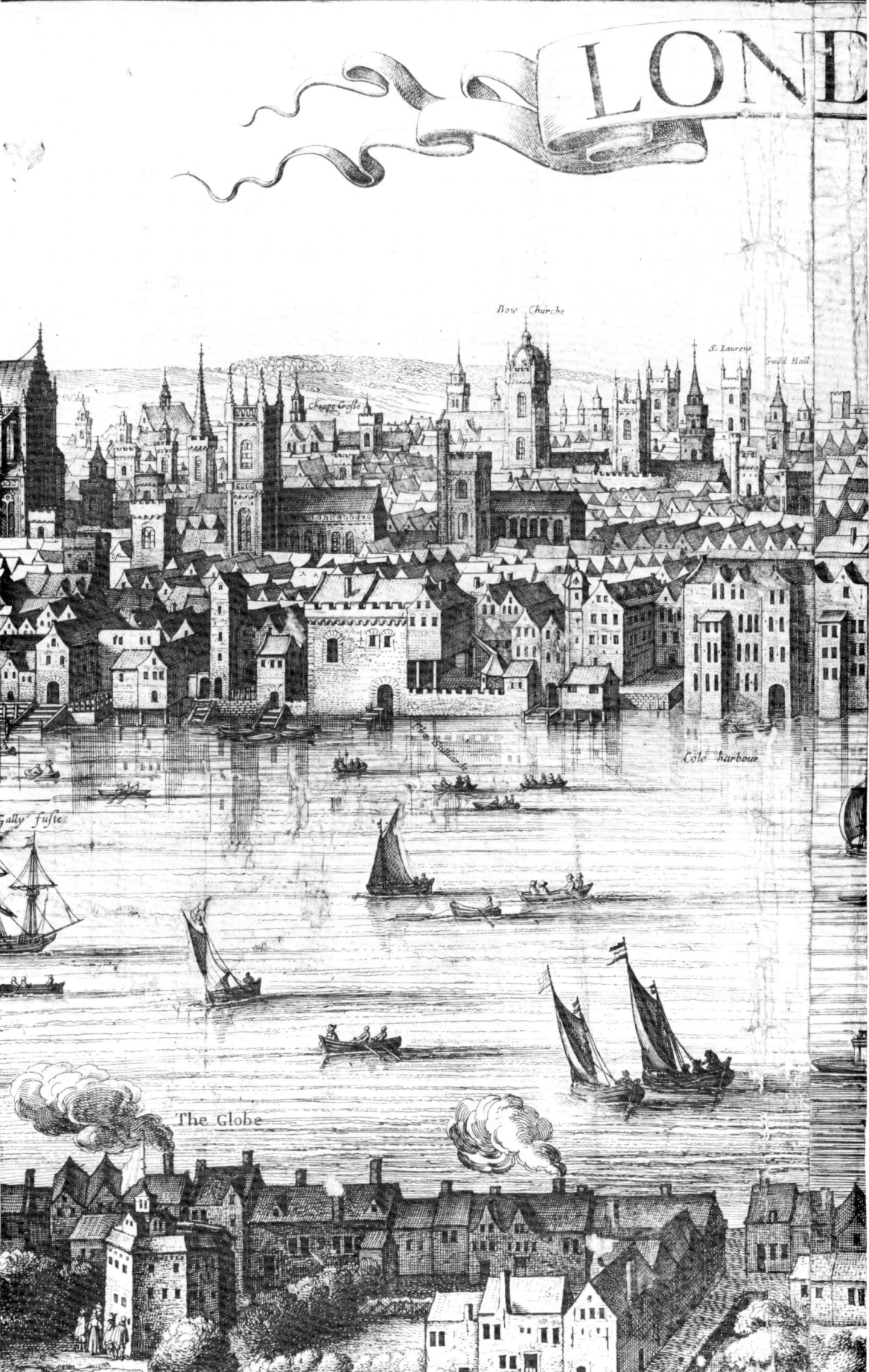

GEOFFREY CHAUCER
The Canterbury Tales
London, William Caxton, ca. 1478

First among the books printed on the "scept'red isle" of Britain was Chaucer's engaging *Tales* of his pilgrims on their journey to Canterbury. This volume was produced by William Caxton in England's first printing shop, located in Westminster at the sign of the Red Pale. Caxton lived for thirty-three years in Bruges. There he acquired the art of printing and produced his first book, his own translation of a medieval romance, *The Recuyell of the Historyes of Troye*, around 1471, only some sixteen to twenty years after Gutenberg's invention. To the great service of literature, Caxton published ninety-six separate works or editions of works almost single-handedly. This edition of *The Canterbury Tales*, which apparently survives in only eleven copies, followed the old manuscript tradition of "rubricating" or rendering in red the large ornamental initial letters which were inked in by hand. **JAG**

Whan that Aprill with his shouris sote
And the droughte of marche hath pad ȝ rote
And badid euery veyne in suche licour
Of whiche vertu engendrid is the flour
Whanne zephirus eke with his sote breth
Enspirid hath in euery holte andȝ heth
The tendir cropis andȝ the yong sonne
Hath in the ram half his cours y ronne
Andȝ smale foulis make melodie
That sleppyn al nyght with oppyn ye
So prikith hem nature in her corage
Than longyng folk to goyn on pilgrimage
Andȝ palmers to seche straunge londis
To serue halowis conthe in sondry londis
Andȝ specially fro euery shiris ende
Of yngelond to Cauntirbury thy wende
The holy blissful martir forto seke
That hem hath holpyn when they were seke
And fil in that sesoun on a day
In Suthwerk atte tabard as I lay
Redy to wende on my pilgrimage
To Cauntirbury with deuout corage
That nyght was come in to that hostery
Wel nyne & twenty in a companye
Of sondry folk be auenture y falle
In felethip as pilgrympys were they alle
That toward Cauntirbury wolden ryde
The chambris andȝ the stablis were wyde
Andȝ wel were they esid atte beste

18

REPLICA OF SHAKESPEARE'S TEMPLE AT GARRICK'S HOME

ca. 1830

David Garrick (1717-1779) was the foremost actor of his day and an organizer of the fabulous Shakespeare Jubilee which took place at Stratford in September of 1769. This jubilee and such shrines as the Shakespeare Temple, which Garrick had built at his home in Hampton, are evidence of the Shakespeare cult which developed in Garrick's time and continues today.

One item in the Folger's collection of Shakespearean curios, this replica of the monument at Garrick's home contains a miniature set of Shakespeare works printed in 1825. A lovely tribute, the replica was said to have been a coronation gift to William IV of England, who reigned from 1830 to 1837. The tiny volumes are stamped with William's coat-of-arms. ***JAG***

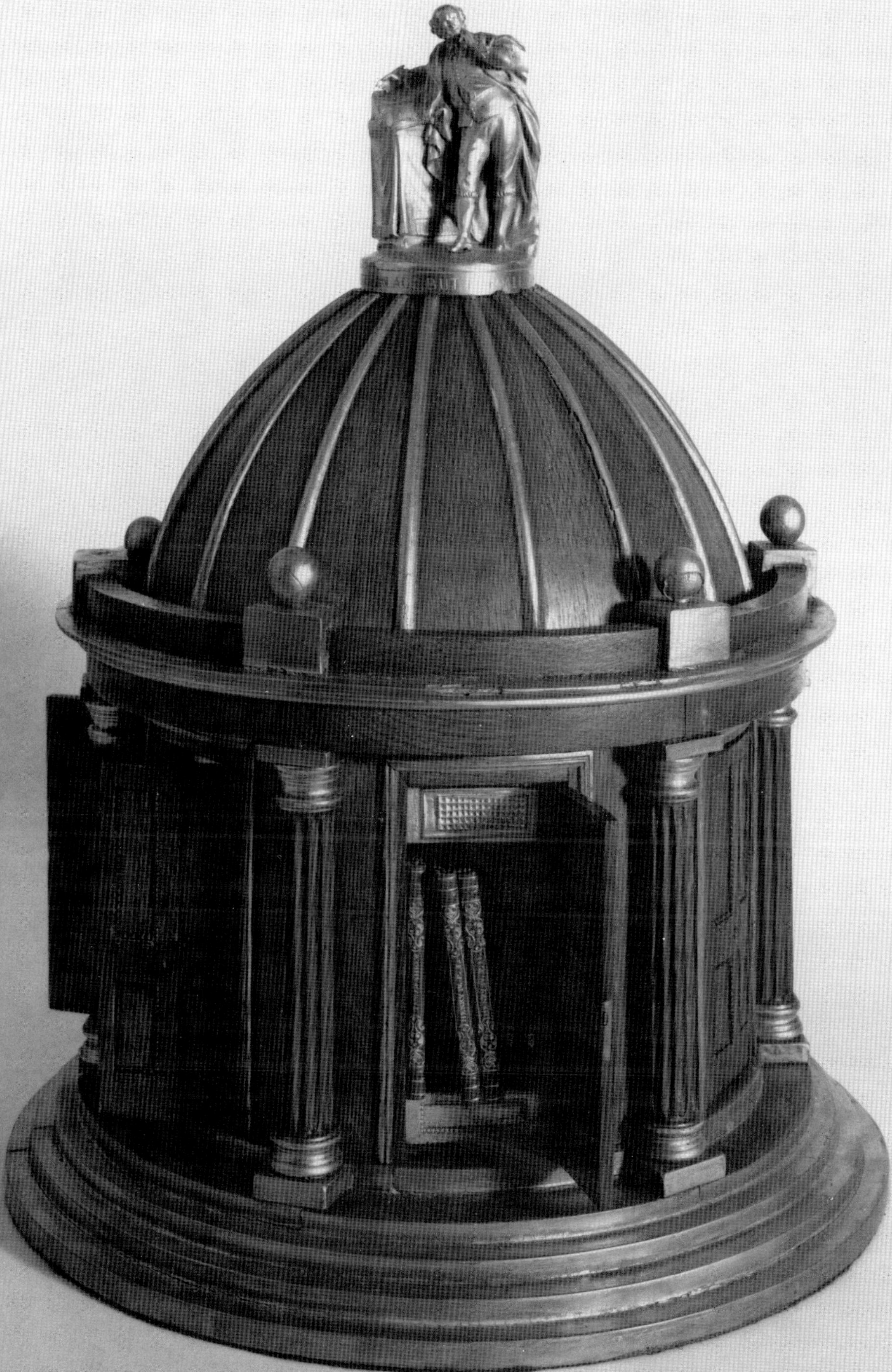

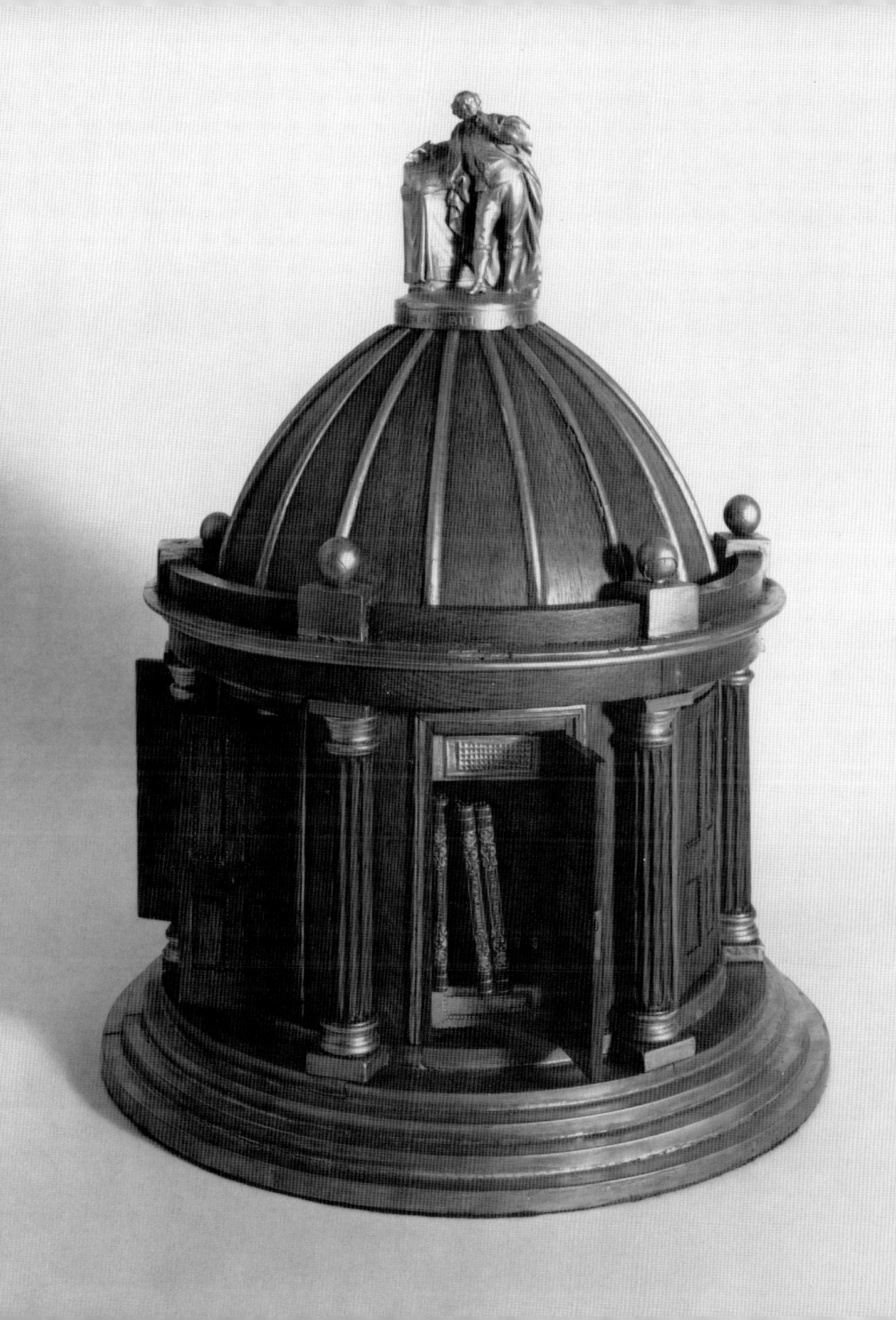

19

SIXTEENTH-CENTURY LUTE

The lute was perhaps the most popular of the Renaissance musical instruments, originating in the Middle East and played all over Europe by the early 15th century. Built in 1598 in Padua, this instrument is a bass lute from the workshop of Michielle Harton, as one can read, in good light, on the interior of the lute, and as indicated by the initials on the face of the instrument. It is of particular interest to performers and scholars, not only because its construction is of extremely high caliber, but also because this lute was formerly owned by Arnold Dolmetsch, a leading figure in the revival of enthusiasm and performance of early music which took place in the beginning of this century.

The instrument is made of thirty-five ribs of shaded yew wood with its brown heartwood and white sapwood cut for purposes of decoration to reveal both colors. The poplar neck and beechwood peg box are veneered with ebony and ivory. Originally a nine-course lute, Dolmetsch modified the instrument, giving it the ten courses increasingly called for in the lute repertoire of the late Elizabethan period and after.   ***JAG***

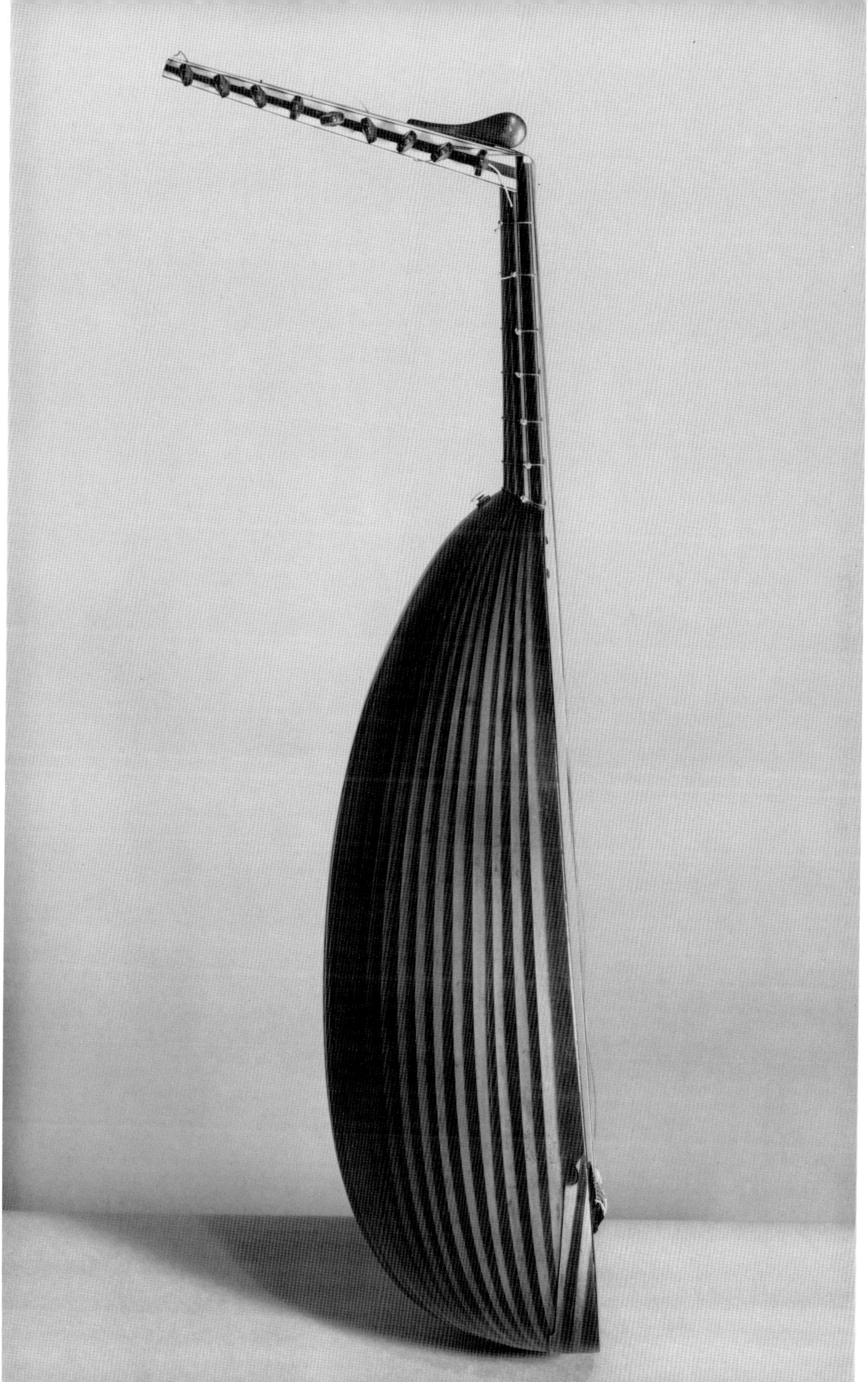

20

PIERRE BELON

L'Histoire de la nature des oyseaux

Paris, Benoist Preuost, 1555

Dr. Pierre Belon (1517-1564) was one of the first experts in comparative anatomy. After studying medicine in Paris and botany in Wittenberg, Belon wrote several valuable scientific works on plants and animals, both fish and fowl, including this beautifully hand-colored book on birds. Belon's studies were so comprehensive, because, in 1546, he undertook an extensive scientific expedition. For three years he traveled through Greece, Asia Minor, Egypt, Arabia, and Palestine, collecting specimens and noting natural phenomena. This scientific expedition foreshadowed those of a later age. The fascinating and informative journal of his travels was published and is also in the Folger collection. ***JAG***

Du Pic verd iaulne.

CHAP. XIII.

NOVS cognoissons deux especes de Pics verds communs en touts lieux. Aristote au neufuiesme chapitre, du neufuiesme liure des animaux en á mis trois, dont celuy que nous nommós le Pic mart, ou Pic verd nous est le plus commun: touteffois qu'en mettrós encor' quelques autres incogneues aux anciens. Le Pic verd iaulne est de longue corpulence, & plus gros qu'vn Loriot, approchant de bien pres celuy d'vne Pie. Il est d'vne exquise couleur diuerse, combien qu'il ne soit de trop bon manger. Il á deux taches rouges dessus les yeux, vne en chasque costé, venant des racines de la partië d'embas de son bec, qui est long de deux doigts, noir, droit, dur, fort, & poinctu : quasi limé en

Picsuerds.

Description du Pic verd.

Dryocolaptos, Pipra, Pipo, Chloreus en Grec, Picus Martius maior, Picus arborarius, & arborum cauator en Latin, Pic mart, Pic verd, ou Pic iaulne en François.

ὁ δ᾽ δρυοκολάπτης ἐ καθίζει ἐπὶ τ̃ γῆς·κόπτει δ᾽ τὰς δρῦς τῶν σκωλήκων κ᾽ σκνιπῶν ἔνεκεν, ἵν᾽ ἐξίωσιν. ἔτερον δ᾽ δρυοκολάπτων γένος μεῖζον ἢ κόπυφος, &c. Arist.lib. 9. cap. 9.

quatre quarres. Laquelle chose Aristote auoit des-ia dit au iiij. liure, *De partibus animalium*, chapitre premier. *Auium cæterarum* (dit il) *rostrum vtile ad victum cuiusque est. Verbi gratia, Roborisecti generis, & Coruini robustum, atque prædurum os est.* Il á la teste asses grosse, & est rouge par dessus, & en chasque costé y á vne tache de plumes blondes, celle part ou sont ses ouyës. Il est verd par dessus les espaules, comme aussi dessus les ælles : mais telle couleur est aussi meslee de iaulne. Celles

21

A MIDSUMMER NIGHT'S DREAM RETOLD

Shakespeare's accomplishment is evident not only in the remarkable words in the plays and poems he wrote, but also in the many and great reverberations of his genius in other creative artists. Among many examples in the Folger collection are these works in various media, all inspired by *A Midsummer Night's Dream*.

The great essayist Charles Lamb and his sister Mary wrote prose versions of Shakespeare's plays for young people, aiming to offer enjoyment as well as "a lesson of all sweet and honourable thoughts and actions"; this little volume published in 1811 is an early edition of the Lambs' tale of Bottom and his friends. Arthur Rackham is among the many visual artists who have painted scenes from Shakespeare's plays. After all of Puck's shenanigans, the lovers are united here in Rackham's beautiful watercolor, done for a 1908 edition of *A Midsummer Night's Dream*. Shakespeare has also inspired great music. Among the most celebrated is Felix Mendelssohn's music for *A Midsummer Night's Dream*. This score for the overture arranged for two performers is Mendelssohn's manuscript copy, signed by the composer. **JAG**

CHARLES LAMB

The Midsummer Night's Dream

London, M.J. Godwin, 1811

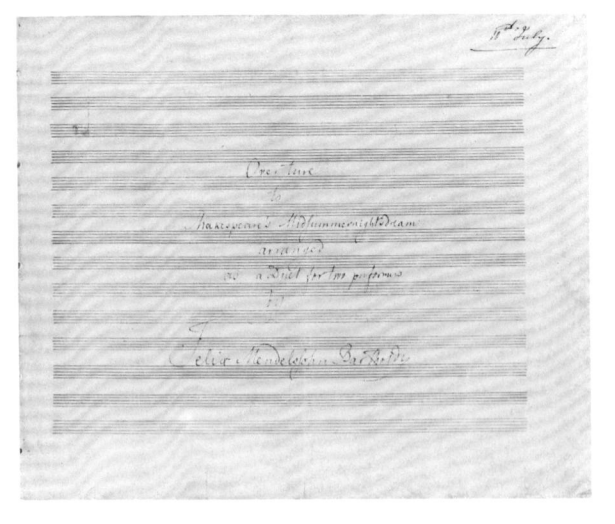

FELIX BARTHOLDY-MENDELSSOHN

Overture to Shakespeare's Midsummernight's dream arranged as a duet for two performers on piano

10 July [1826?]

ARTHUR RACKHAM

"Are you sure that we are awake. . . .?"

London, William Heinmann, 1908

22

BIBLIA GERMANICA

Nuremberg, Anton Koberger, 17 Feb., 1483

This beautifully illustrated volume is one of the earliest Bibles published in vernacular German. This is significant because it indicated a growing effort on the part of some to make the scriptures available to laymen as well as to the clergy. It was the first book with illustrations printed by the Anton Koberger firm, which also produced the *Nuremberg Chronicles*, also included in this exhibition. The 109 woodcut illustrations have all been hand-colored. Initial capital letters are inked in blue and red and in some sections illuminated in gold. This Bible is a fine example of the Folger's collection of *incunabula* (from the Latin meaning *cradle*) or books printed before 1501, when printing was in its infancy. ***JAG***

Dauid   In dem

Ein andere vorred.

Ich bin gewesen der aller iungst vnd mein brüdern. vnd bin gewesen der künig iungling i dē hawse meins vaters. Ich hab gewaydet die schaff meins vaters. mein hend habē gemacht ein orgel. vn̄ mein vinger haben bereytet einen psalter. Vn̄ wer ist d. der meinē herrē hat verkündet vn̄ gesaget von mir. der herr aller herrē selber hat mich erhöret. Er hat gesant eine engel. vn̄ hat mich gefürt. vn̄ hindan genomen vō den schaffen meines vaters. vnd er hat mich gesalbet mit der salben seiner Barmhertzigkeyt. Mein brüder waren gut vn̄ groß. vnd dē herre was nit ein wolgeuallen in in. Ich bin außgegangen. vn̄ entgegen kume dē heydē philisteo. Vnd hab aufgezogen das schwert von seiner scheyde. vnd hab im abgeschlagen sein haubt. Vnd also genomen das laster vnd die schand von dēn kindern von israhel.

Ein end habē dy vorred.

Vn̄ hebt an d' künigklich prophet dauid. der erst titel des ersten psalms.

Da saul gots gebott brach. da sant er samuelē. das er wehet dauid im zu einem künig. da das geschah da zoh der heylig geyst von saul. Vn̄ da man dauid satzt auf des reichs stul zu bethleem. da machet er disen ersten psalmen. Wī got die gerechten vn̄ guten leytet. dy seyne wert vnd sein gebot halten. vnd wie die bösen. dy in verlassen. werdē verleitet. Vn̄ dy vbergeschrift ditz psalms ist. d psalm dauid.

Nocturn an dem suntag.
Beatus vir qui.   Der erst psalm

Selig ist der mann der nicht abgieng in dē rat der vngütige vn̄ nicht stund i dē weg d' sund. vn̄ nicht saß in dē stull der pestilentz. Sunder sein will ist in d' ee des herre. vnd in seiner ee wirt er betrachtē tag vn̄ nacht. Vn̄ er wirt als d3 hostz. das da ist gepflantzet bey dē ablauff d' wasser. das sein frucht wirdt geben in seiner zeyt. Vn̄ sein laub wirt nit absließen. vn̄ alle dig dy er wirdt thun werde glückša. O ir vngütige nit also nit also. aber als d' staub den der wind verwürfft vō dē antlytz der erde Darūb die vngüttige ersteen nit in dem vrteyl. noch die sunder in dē rat der gerechtē. Wann der herre hat erkant dē weg der gerechtigkeyt vnd der steyge der vngüttige wirdt verderben.

Disen psalm machet dauid

do er vechten solt wider amalech. vn̄ wider dye heydēn philiste. Vn̄ ditz psalms vbergeschrift ist. der psalm dauid.

ORLANDO FVRIOSO
DI M. LVDOVICO ARIOSTO
nouissimamente alla sua integrità ridot=
to & ornato di varie figure.
CON ALCVNE STANZE DEL S.
Aluigi Gonzaga in lode del medesimo.
AGGIVNTOVI PER CIASCVN
Canto alcune allegorie & nel fine
vna breue espositione
ET TAVOLA DI TVTTO
quello, che nell'opera si contiene
CON GRATIA ET PRIVILEGIO.

IN VENETIA APPRESSO GABRIEL
GIOLITO DI FERRARII
M. D. XLIII.

23

LUDOVICO ARIOSTO
Orlando Furioso
Venice, Giolito de Ferrari, 1544

Published in three versions (1516, 1521, 1532), the *Orlando Furioso* is the masterpiece of Italy's greatest Renaissance poet. Combining motifs from both Carolingian and Arthurian epic traditions, and continuing the narrative begun in Matteo Maria Boiardo's *Orlando Innamorato* (1483, 1495), Ariosto created an altogether original version of the epic poem—wise, witty, and fully consistent with the worldly outlook of contemporary urban and courtly elites. Louise George Clubb has described it as "the funniest and saddest of poems, personal and detached, simple and artful." It profoundly influenced Spenser's *Faerie Queene*, and inspired operatic and visual adaptations for centuries. One of the most beautiful of many editions in the Folger Library, this sumptuous copy was printed on special blue paper, with gilt hand-lettered initials and decorations throughout. Shown here is Dolci's sonnet in praise of Ariosto, with the frontispiece of the appended commentary. **WG**

JOHN CALVIN

Institutio Christianae Religionis together with the same author's *Harmonia ex tribus Evangelistis composita*

Geneva, Robert Stephanus, 1559-1560

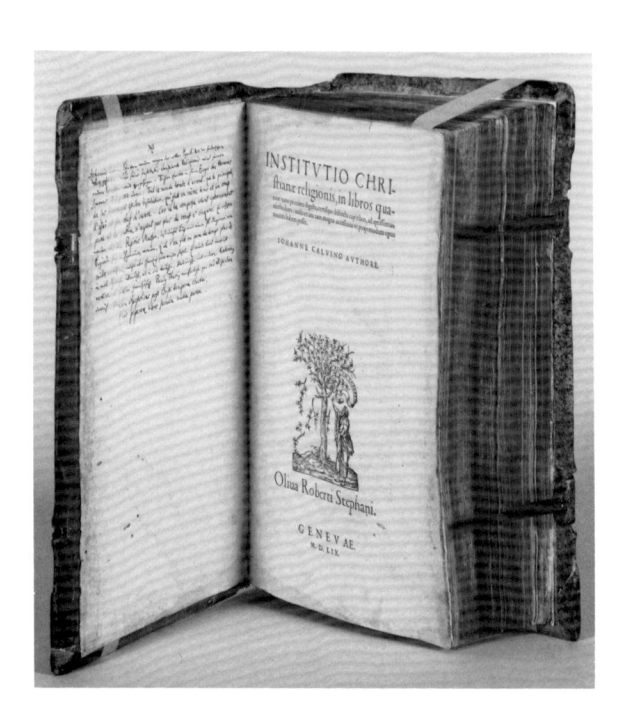

This great volume, bound in wooden boards covered with contemporary bleached and hand-tooled leather, with clasps, contains Calvin's most important theological works. The *Institutes of the Christian Religion* has been described as the Protestant *summa theologica*. It first appeared in print in 1536, but Calvin was constantly engaged in changing and expanding it, until it reached its definitive shape in the present edition, which appeared five years before the reformer's death. The Folger copy, acquired in 1957, contains underlinings and marginalia in several different early hands, both in Latin and Greek. In its French and other vernacular versions, the *Institutes* became one of the theological best-sellers of early modern Europe. It still provides the basis for Calvinist and Presbyterian doctrine. **WG**

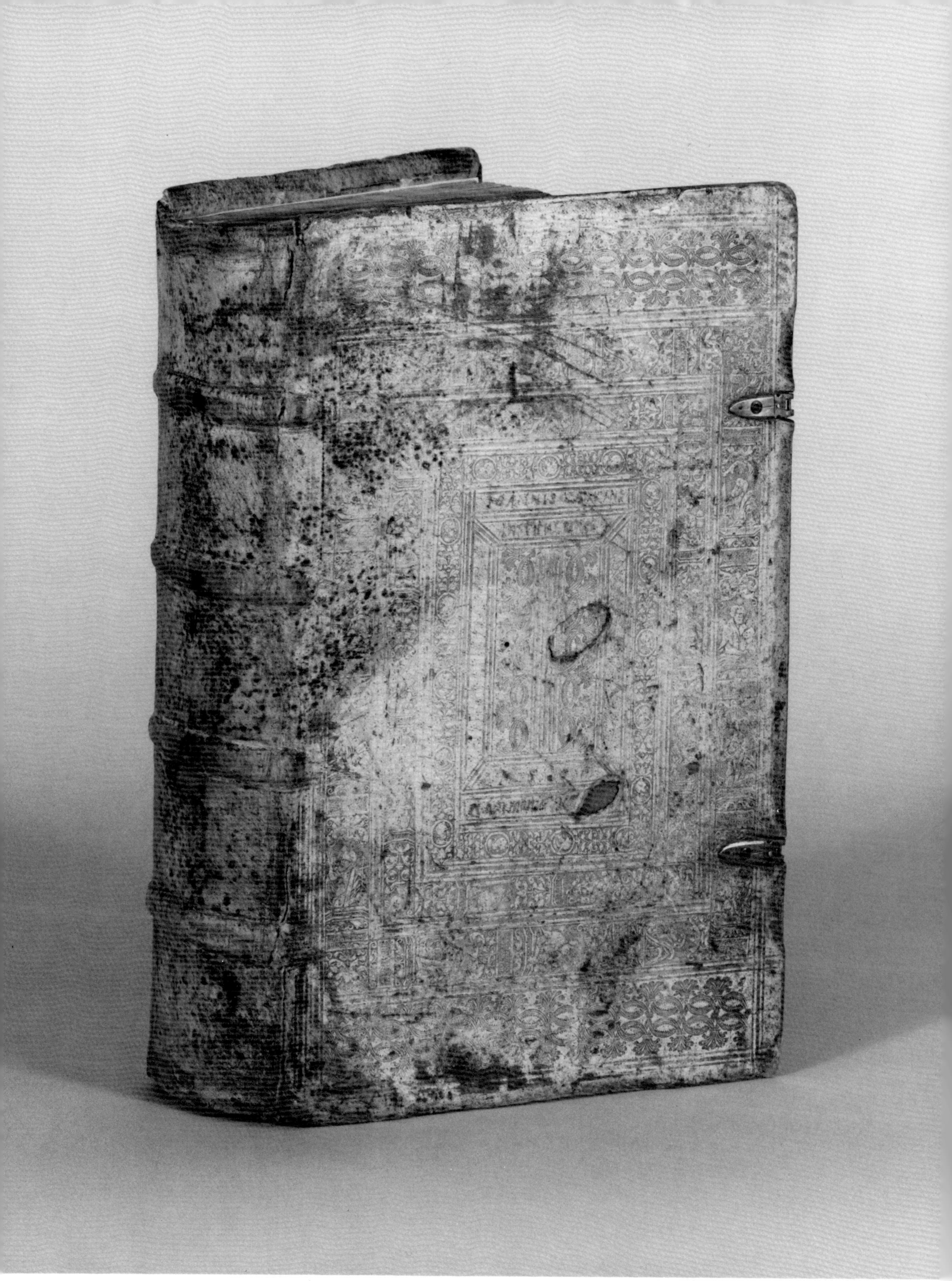

MARTIN LUTHER

Ad Leonem X Pontificem Maximum Resolutiones disputationum de virtute indulgentiarum

Wittenberg, October, 1518

For many years, the Folger has been one of the best places in which to study the Protestant Reformation. The library's extensive holdings of Reformation books and pamphlets grew by over 900 rare titles in 1977, when it acquired the collection of rare German materials compiled by the Swiss collector Emanuel Stickelberger. Within that collection, the works of Martin Luther represent a particular strength. This volume includes eight of Luther's treatises and sermons from 1518. It demonstrates how deeply, within a year of his Ninety-Five Theses, the young monk had become enmeshed in theological controversy. It also shows, even typographically, the straightforward, pugnacious character of Luther's style, his absolute fearlessness in challenging established authority. His was not the first nor by far the last effort by a Doctor of Sacred Theology to seek to persuade the Pope to modify an important doctrine. **WG**

AD LEONEM X·
PONTIFICEM MAXIMVM,

⁌ Resolutiones disputationum de uirtute indulgentia
rum reuerēdi patris ac sacræ Theologiæ doctoris Mar
tini Luther Augustiniani Vuittenbergensis.

⁌ Fratris patris Siluestri Prieratis ordinis prædicato
rum Magiri sacri Palacij ad Martinum Dialogus.

⁌ R.P. Martini Luther ad eum Dialogũ Responsio.

⁌ Contra D. Ioannem Eckium Ingoldstadiensem So
phisticum argutatorem, Apologeticæ propositiones
D. Andreæ Bodenstein Archidiaconi Vuittēbergēn.

⁌ R.P. Martini Luther, Sermo de pœnitentia.

⁌ Sermo de indulgentijs.

⁌ Sermo de uirtute excommunicationis.

⁌ Decē præcepta Vuittenbergensi populo prædicata.
Et alia quædam.

FRANCESCO PETRARCA

Il Petrarcha: Con l'espositione d'Allessandro Vellutello di novo ristampato con le figure a i triomphi, et con piu cose utili in varii luoghi aggiunte

Venice, Giolito de Ferrari, 1545

On the endpapers of this book, a tidy eighteenth-century hand has written: "Petrarch (the Poet the Italians bragg most on) borrowed most of his language and Poetry from the Poets of Provence. . . ." Yet, these impressive and influential stanzas also derive clearly from the idea of Roman imperial processions. Celebrating such conditions as love, chastity, death, and fame, these great fourteenth-century Tuscan poems affected European writers for centuries. By the time the Folger's edition appeared, Petrarch's verse had already become the subject of commentary as well as widespread imitation.
WG

IL PETRARCHA

CON L'ESPOSITIONE
D'ALESSANDRO VELLVTELLO
DI NOVO RISTAMPATO CON LE FIGV-
RE A I TRIOMPHI, ET CON PIV COSE
VTILI IN VARII LVOGHI AGGIVNTE.

IN VINEGIA APPRES
SO GABRIEL GIOLITO
DE FERRARI
MDXXXXV.

DESIDERIUS ERASMUS
Moriae Encomium, or *Stultitiae Laus*
Basel, Iohannes Froben, 1519

The Praise of Folly is Erasmus' best-known work. This would have surprised, and almost surely displeased the great Dutch humanist, for whom it was a diversion from such weighty matters as translations and editions of Scripture, commentaries on the Church Fathers, and other books of classial and patristic philology. In its mordant satire on the pretensions and pomposities of church and state, its acute lampooning of human foibles, and its complex and witty style, it recalls such ancient masters as Lucian while anticipating (and instructing) Swift. In the high seriousness of its concluding evangelical message, it encapsulates the spiritual yearning of many cultivated Europeans on the eve of the Reformation. The author personally supervised the printing of many of his works in the Froben shop, quite possibly including this one. **WG**

IO·FRO

BENIVS LECTO-
RI S. D.

Habes iterū Moriæ enco
miū, pro castigatissimo ca
stigatius, unà cū Listrij cómen
tarijs, & alijs complusculis libel
lis, non minus eruditis ꝙ festi
uis: quorum catalogum proxi-
ma mox indicabit pagella. Bene uale.

APVD INCLYTAM BA-
SILEAM M̄. D̄. XIX.

GIOVANNI BOCCACCIO
Il Decamerone
Venice, Giolito de Ferrari, 1552

One of the great short story collections of all time, the *Decameron* is an invaluable source for literary scholars and historians alike. It is a collection of one hundred tales told over a period of ten days in 1348 by a group of ten young Florentines. In order to escape the Black Death, they have taken refuge at an elegant country house. There they regale each other with lively accounts that illuminate the social behavior and attitudes of fourteenth-century Italians. Many of the stories lampoon the clergy and satirize middle-class mores and values. The introduction to the *Decameron* provides the most accurate and extensive description of the Black Death and its social consequences to come down to us from Renaissance Florence. Many of its tales inspired later cultural artifacts—poems, plays, and pictures. The stories themselves establish the narrative form on which much short fiction later came to be based. Some derived from and others came to be embedded in the popular folklore of Western Europe. Shown here is an illustration from a fine sixteenth-century edition depicting the famous story of Nastagio degli Onesti, which Botticelli had previously depicted in a series of three memorable panels. **WG**

IL DECAMERONE
DI M. GIOVANNI
BOCCACCIO.

NVOVAMENTE ALLA SVA VERA
LETTIONE RIDOTTO.
CON TVTTE QVELLE ALLEGORIE, ANNOTA-
tioni, e tauole, che nelle altre nostre impressioni si conten-
gono; e di piu ornato di molte figure.
AGGIVNTOVI SEPARATAMENTE VN'INDICE
copiosissimo d'i uocaboli e delle materie composto
da Messer Lodouico Dolce.

CON GRATIA ET PRIVILEGIO.

IN VINEGIA APPRESSO GABRIEL
GIOLITO DE FERRARI, ET
FRATELLI. MDLII.

MICHEL EYQUEM DE MONTAIGNE
Les Essais
Paris, Abel l'Angelier, 1598

This edition of the *Essays* is fairly typical of the many versions published in the years immediately following the author's death in 1593. The very idea of the essay, the form itself, was a product of one of Europe's fiercely original minds. While fully conversant with all of the intellectual currents of his own tumultuous times, and steeped in the writings of the ancients, Montaigne approached every topic with a fresh, iconoclastic outlook. Common sense and sensory experience for him far outweighed received authority, whether secular or religious. In choosing himself as his subject, he touches virtually everything else under the sun. His gentle irony is clear from the beginning as he informs his reader: "I am myself the matter of my book; you would be unreasonable to spend your leisure on so frivolous and vain a subject." **WG**

ESSAIS DE MICHEL DE MONTAIGNE,

LIVRE PREMIER.

Par diuers moyens on arriue à pareille fin.

Chap. I.

LA plus commune façon d'amollir les cœurs de ceux qu'on a offensez, lors qu'ayants la vēgeance en main, ils nous tiennēt à leur mercy, c'est de les esmouuoir par submission, à cōmiseration & à pitié : Toutesfois la brauerie, la cōstance, resolution, moyens tous contraires, ont quelquesfois seruy à ce mesme effect. Edouard Prince de Vvalles, celuy qui regenta si long temps nostre Guienne: personnage duquel les cōditions & la fortune ont beaucoup de notables parties de grandeur; ayant esté bien fort offensé par les Limosins, & prenant leur ville par force, ne peut estre arresté par les cris du peuple, & des femmes, & enfans abandonnez à la boucherie, luy criants mercy, & se iettants à ses pieds : iusqu'à ce que passant tousiours outre dans la ville, il apperceut trois gentils-hōmes François, qui d'vne hardiesse incroyable soustenoient seuls l'effort de son armee victorieuse. La consideration & le respect d'vne si notable vertu, reboucha premierement la pointe de sa cholere : & commença par ces trois, à faire misericorde à tous les autres habitans de la ville. Scanderberch, Prince de l'Epire, suiuant vn soldat des siens pour le tuer, & ce soldat ayant essayé par toute espece d'humilité & de supplication de l'appaiser, se resolut

A

MIGUEL DE CERVANTES SAAVEDRA

El Ingenioso Hidalgo Don Quixote de la Mancha

Brussels, Roger Velpius and Huberto Antonio, 1611

A universal classic and arguably the greatest book ever written in Spanish, *Don Quixote* is far too little read in this country. An instantaneous popular success, it appeared in French, German, Italian, and English translations within seven years of its completion. It is interesting to realize that the first modern novel was composed by a sick, aged, and impoverished man, who believed that a satirical tale might produce more revenue than the poems and plays that he regarded as his more serious mission. Under the guise of a parody on romances of chivalry, Cervantes created a study of reality and illusion, madness and sanity, that links him with such acute sixteenth-century students of psychology as Erasmus, Rabelais, Montaigne, and Shakespeare. This copy, one of the earliest printed in the Low Countries, is opened to the celebrated Chapter Eight, "Of the good fortune which the valorous Don Quixote had in the terrifying and never-before-imagined adventure of the windmills, along with other events that deserve to be suitably recorded." The extensive marginal notes await study. **WG**

EL
INGENIOSO
HIDALGO DON
QVIXOTE DE LA
MANCHA.

COMPVESTO POR
Miguel de Ceruantes Saauedra.

*DIRIGIDO AL DVQVE
de Bejar, Marquez de Gibraleon, Conde de
Benalcaçar, y Bañares, Vizconde de la
Puebla de Alcozer, Señor de las
villas de Capilla, Curiel,
y Burguillos.*

EN BRVCELAS,
Por Roger Velpius y Huberto Antonio, Impressores de sus Altezas, en l'Aguila de oro, cerca
de Palacio, Año 1611.

LOUIS LE ROY

De la vicissitude ou variete des choses en l'univers, et concurrence des armes et des lettres par les premieres et plus illustres nations du monde, depuis le temps où à commencé la civilité iusques À present

Paris, Pierre l'Huilier, 1575

Louis Le Roy (1510?-1577), Royal Professor of Greek in the University of Paris, won fame as a biographer, translator of Plato and Aristotle, and political pamphleteer during the Wars of Religion. But he was best known for this extraordinary work of universal history, in which he traces the rise and fall of civilizations to their preeminence in arms and letters. An early advocate of the idea of progress, as well as the comparative method, Le Roy probably influenced Montaigne and Bacon. This is the rare first edition of the *Vicissitude*. Followed by many other printings, it was also translated into Italian and English. An early believer in religious toleration, Le Roy nevertheless had something of a reputation for a haughty and sarcastic personal style, a fact noted inside the front cover by an early owner of this copy. **WG**

Le bon Dieu soit mon protecteur

DE LA VICISSITVDE
OV VARIETE DES CHOSES
EN L'VNIVERS, ET CONCVRRENCE DES
ARMES ET DES LETTRES PAR LES PREMIERES ET
plus illustres nations du monde, depuis le temps où à commencé la ciuilité, & memoire humaine iusques à present.

PLVS S'IL EST VRAY NE SE DIRE RIEN QVI
n'ayt esté dict parauant: & qu'il conuient par propres inuentions augmenter la doctrine des anciens, sans s'arrester seulement aux versiõs, expositions, corrections, & abregez de leurs escrits.

PAR LOYS LE ROY DICT REGIVS.

AV TRES-CHRESTIEN ROY DE FRANCE ET DE
Poloigne Henry III. du nom.

A PARIS,
Chez Pierre l'Huilier, rue S. Iacques à l'Oliuier.
1575.
Auec priuilege du Roy.

THOMAS MORE

De optimo reip. statu, deque nova insula Utopia, libellus vere aureus....

Basel, Iohannes Froben, December, 1518

More and Erasmus were close friends. In fact, although Erasmus claimed to have written *The Praise of Folly* during a trip across the Alps, we now know that it was composed while Erasmus was More's house guest in Chelsea. Its Greek title, *Moriae Encomion*, puns on More's name. *Utopia* was written in a similar spirit of social and religious questioning. The first serious Utopian treatise since Plato's *Republic*, it gave its name to a genre of social and political theory and practice that is still with us. With its egalitarianism and its emphasis on communal ownership of property, More's work has long been claimed by Marxist critics as a forerunner of modern socialism. However, these radical concepts can all be traced to early Christian sources, and to medieval texts such as the Rule of St. Benedict. The woodcuts in this book have traditionally been attributed to Hans Holbein. **WG**

Amaurotū vrbs.

Fons Anydri.   Ostium anydri.

hythlodaeus.

NICCOLO MACHIAVELLI

Il Principe de Niccholo Machiavello al Magnifico Lorenzo di Piero de Medici

Rome, Antonio Blado d'Asolo, January 4, 1532

This unprepossessing volume contains the first printing of a work described as "a knife driven into the flank of Europe, causing it to shriek and rear up." Circulated in manuscript after its composition in 1513, *The Prince* first became widely available five years after its author's death in 1527. Contrary to opinions still widely held today, Machiavelli was neither an atheist nor an advocate of unrestrained cruelty or deceit. However, basing his views on a study of Roman history and current affairs, he sought to be useful to a new ruler by describing how things actually work, rather than how they ought to be. This led to a reputation for cynicism and immorality which can only be justified in small part. Shown here is the famous seventeenth chapter, "Of cruelty and mercy, and whether it is better to be loved or feared." **WG**

spender quel d'altri non toglie riputatione, ma tene aggiugne, sola
mente lo spender il tuo è quello che ti nuoce, & non ce cosa che con
sumi se stessa quanto la liberalità. la qual mentre che tù l'usi, perdi
la facultà d'usarla, & diuenti ò, puuero ò, contennendo, ò per fug
gir la pouertà, rapace, & odioso, Et intra tutte le cose da che un
Principe si debbe guardare, è l'esser contennendo, & odioso, & la
liberalità, à l'una, & l'altra di queste cose ti conduci. Per tanto è
più sapientia tenersi il nome di misero, che partorisce una infamia
senza odio, che per uoler il nome di liberale, incorrer per necessità
nel nome di rapace, che partorisce una infamia con odio.

DELLA CRVDELTA, ET CLEMENTIA,
& se gli è meglio esser amato, ò temuto.
Cap. XVII.

ESCEDENDO appresso à l'altre qualità preallega
te Dico che ciascuno Principe deue desiderar d'esser pie
toso tenuto, & non crudele. Nondimanco, deue aduertir
di non usar male questa pietà. Era tenuto Cesare Borgia crudele,
nondimanco quella sua crudeltà haueua racconcia la Romagna, unito
la, ridottola in pace, & in fede. Il che se si considerrà bene, si uedrà
quello esser stato molto più pietoso, che il Popol Fiorentino qual
per fuggir il nome di crudele lasciò distrugger Pistoia. Deue per
tanto un Principe non si curar de l'infamia di crudele per tener i
sudditi suoi uniti, & in fede. Perche con pochissimi essempi sarà più
pietoso, che quelli, li quali per troppa pietà lasciano seguir i disordi
ni, onde naschino occisioni, ò rapine, perche queste sogliono offendere
una universita intiera, & quelle esecutioni che uengono dal Princi
pe offendono un particular. Et infra tutti è Principi al Principe
nuouo è impossibile fuggir il nome di crudele per esser li stati nuoui
pieni di pericoli, onde Virgilio p la bocca di Didone escusa le inhuma
nità del suo Regno, per essere quel nuouo Dicendo Res dura,
& Regni nouitas me talia cogunt, Moliri, & late fines custode tueri.
Non dimeno deue esser graue al creder, & al mouersi, ne si deue
far paura da se stesso, & proceder in modo temperato con pruden
tia, & humanità, che la troppa confidentia non lo faccia incauto,
& la troppa diffidentia non lo renda intollerabile. **Nasce da questo**

ESTHER INGLIS

Octonaries upon the vanity and inconstancy of the world

Dec. 23, 1607

The famous calligrapher and miniaturist, Esther Inglis, was born in France in 1571. Following the massacre of St. Bartholomew in 1572, her family fled to England where the family name was anglicized from Langlois. It is believed that Esther Inglis was, at one time, a nurse to young prince Henry, son of King James I. It is certain that she learned her art from her mother at an age when it was fashionable for ladies of culture to become calligraphers. Her calligraphy exhibits exquisite skill and beauty. The *Octonaries* are a collection of forty-seven poems, each having a verse of eight lines and each with a hand-painted floral design above the poem. The calligraphy is done in several styles including microscopic writing and two written backwards. Many of her manuscripts have survived including four in the Folger Library's collection. The modern calligrapher may admire her work as did her patrons which included Queen Elizabeth I, Elizabeth's ministers, and the royal family of Scotland.   *RL*

OCTO. X.

When as the witherd leaf doth fall
And wan-hewd Autumne doth apall
And with fowle tawny spots desgrace
The beautie off the faire yeares face
Their maye (as in glas) be seene
Thy lyfe, ô wordling! Some tymes greene.
And sometymes faded and forlorne
As yow no fruict nor leafe had borne.

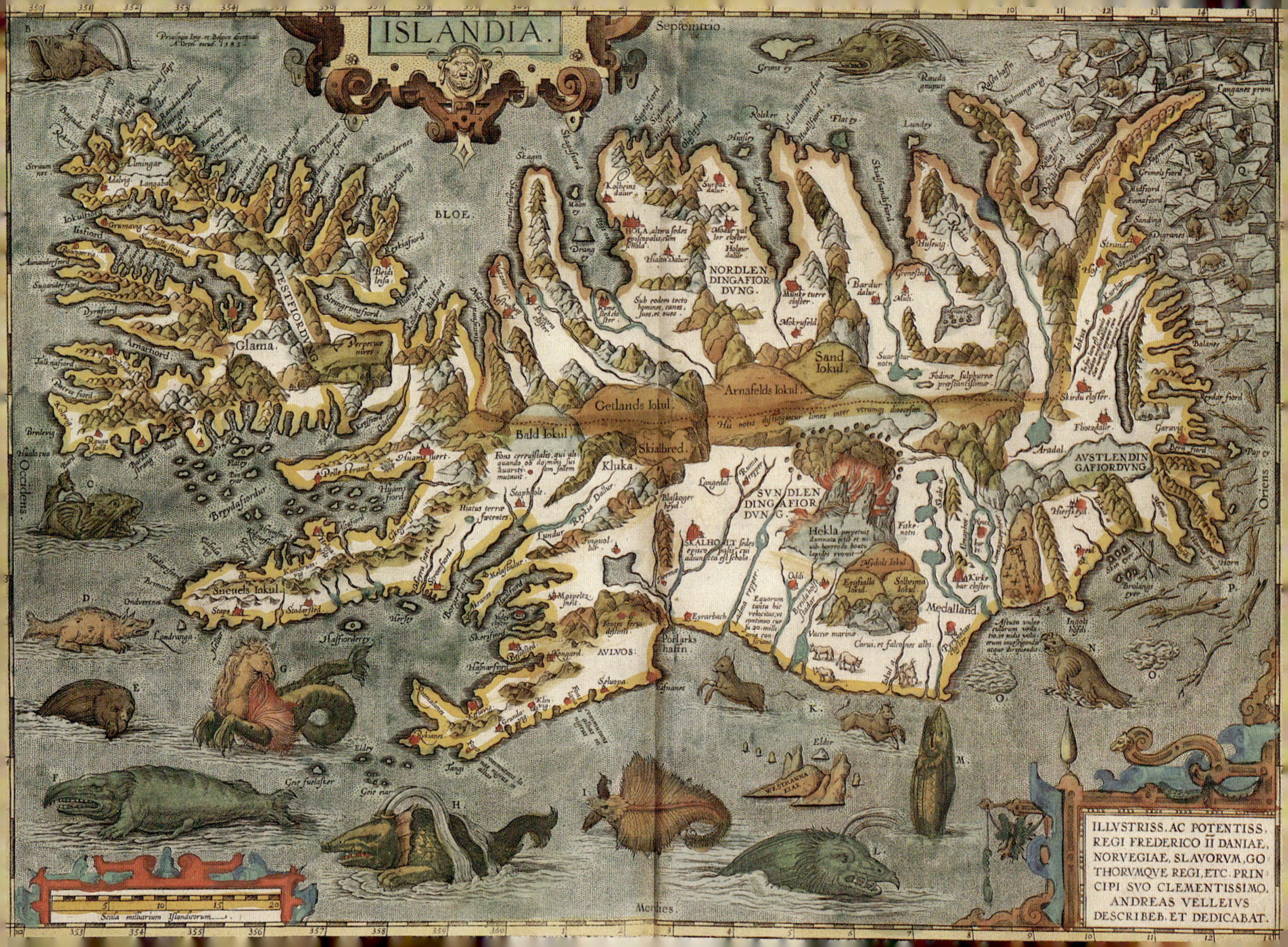

ABRAHAM ORTELIUS
The theatre of the whole world. . . .

London, Iohn Norton, 1606

The Antwerp cartographer Abraham Ortelius first produced a hand-colored edition of maps in May 1570. In so doing, he set a precedent that other publishers of map collections were to emulate well into the 17th century. Ortelius's *Theatre of the whole world* or *Theatrum orbis terrarum* is the first uniform modern atlas of the world. He was very selective in his choice of maps, collecting them from skilled artists. Also remarkable is the accompanying text to each map. In the text he provided contemporary information on each country as well as descriptions by ancient writers. His text was so well received that he was encouraged to publish it separately.

The first edition of 1570 contained seventy maps. This English edition, first published in 1606, eight years after Ortelius's death, has well over a hundred maps. The engraving of Islandia (Iceland) is interesting because of the aquatic life and the polar bears the artist has depicted. The title page is attributed to Frans Hogenberg, who along with his assistants, produced nearly all of the copperplates for the maps in the first edition. ***RL***

JOHN DOWLAND

The first booke of songes and ayres of fowre partes with tableture for the lute

[London], Peter Short, 1597

In 1597 John Dowland, the celebrated English composer and lutenist, published this collection of twenty-one songs arranged so that they could be sung by a solo voice and lute or as four-part airs. This *First booke of songes* was an immediate success and over the following sixteen years was reprinted at least five times. His music continues to be printed and enjoyed today.

Dowland was admired for his beautiful melodic compositions and harmonious tunes and received lauds from his fellow composers and English writers. Around 1598 he was appointed lutenist at the court of the Danish king, Christian IV. It is interesting to note that in spite of his success, Dowland was unable to fulfill his consuming ambition to receive a royal appointment from the English court until fifteen years after the publication of his first book of songs. In October of 1612, he was at last appointed one of the King's lutenists. It was not unusual for 16th-century English music to be printed so that the singers and musicians could sit around a table. In this way, the entire song with all its parts could fit on one opening, thereby avoiding the turning of pages. *RL*

CANTUS

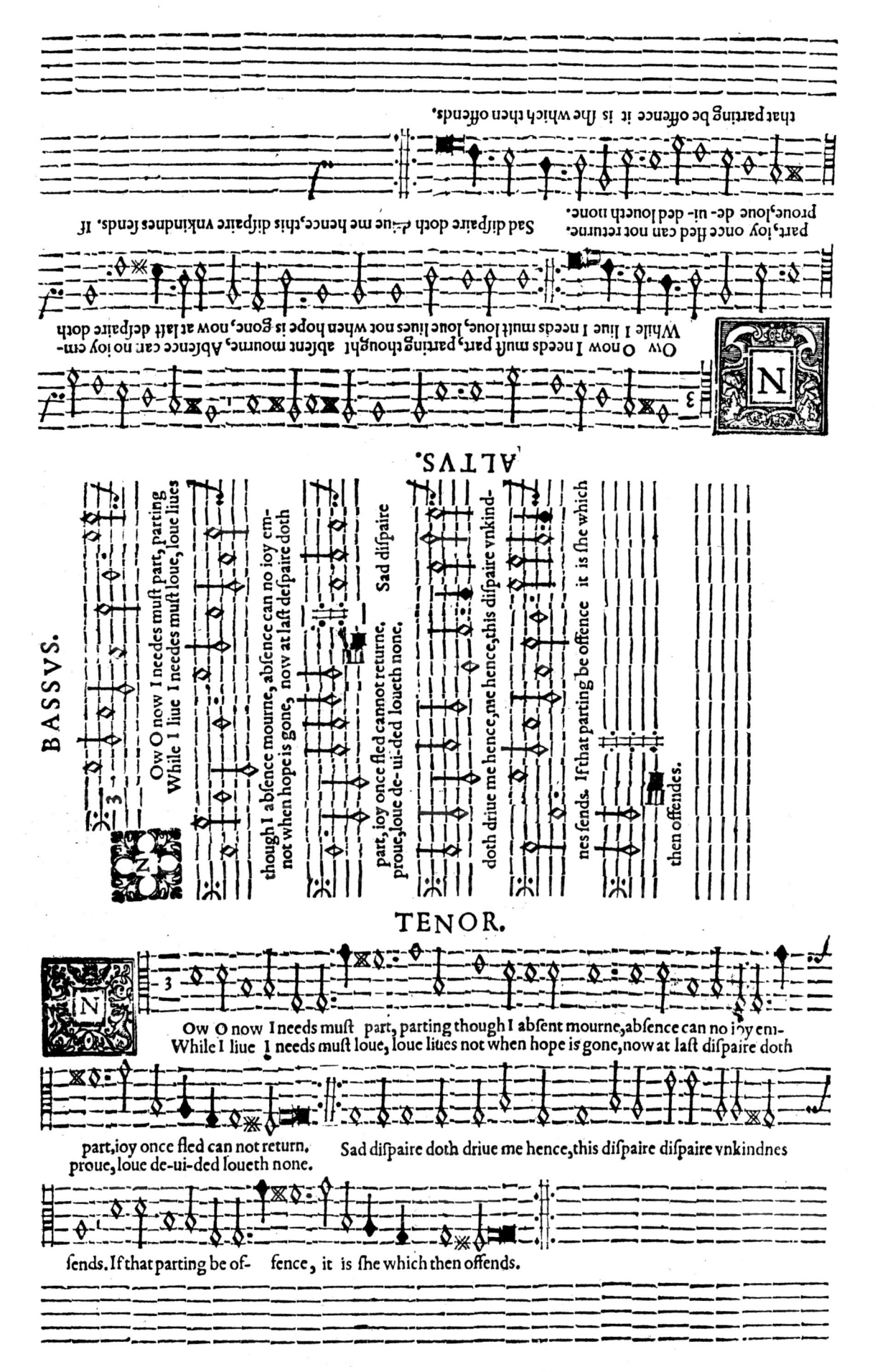

Ow O now I needs must part, parting though I absent mourne, Absence can no ioy em-
While I liue I needs must loue, loue liues not when hope is gone, now at last despaire doth

Sad dispaire doth driue me hence, this dispaire vnkindnes sends. If
proue, loue de-ui-ded loueth none.
part, ioy once fled can not returne.

that parting be offence it is she which then offends.

BASSVS.

Ow O now I needes must part, parting
While I liue I needes must loue, loue liues

though I absence mourne, absence can no ioy em-
not when hope is gone, now at last despaire doth

Sad dispaire
part, ioy once fled cannot returne,
proue, loue de-ui-ded loueth none.

doth driue me hence, this dispaire vnkindnes sends. If that parting be offence it is she which

then offendes.

ALTVS.

TENOR.

Ow O now I needs must part, parting though I absent mourne, absence can no ioy em-
While I liue I needs must loue, loue liues not when hope is gone, now at last dispaire doth

part, ioy once fled can not return. Sad dispaire doth driue me hence, this dispaire dispaire vnkindnes
proue, loue de-ui-ded loueth none.

sends. If that parting be of- fence, it is she which then offends.

D

37

CHARLES PERRAULT

Festiva ad capita annulumque decursio, a rege Ludovico XIV. . . .

Parisiis, E typographica regia, 1670

In this beautifully engraved festival book, Charles Perrault has captured one of the distinguishing features of the reign of Louis XIV, namely, his love for grand fetes and pageants. Louis XIV commissioned Perrault to chronicle this "Grand Carrousel," a carrousel being a display of skillful horsemanship, military maneuvers, and riding with the lance at a ring. This horse show and tournament was staged over a three-day period in June 1662 and was repeated later in the summer. In addition to celebrating the birth of his son, the Grand Dauphin of France, Louis XIV's objective was to exhibit to the world his country's military strength and skill. Louis XIV led the troop of Romans disguised as Rex Romanae Imperator. Other members of the nobility masqueraded as Persians, Turks, Indians, and native Americans and led their costumed troops. Perrault's work provides the modern scholar with an excellent record of the lavishness and grandeur of the court of Louis XIV. The Folger Library has a large collection of festival books, most containing elaborate illustrations of royal processions, tournaments, and pageants.   ***RL***

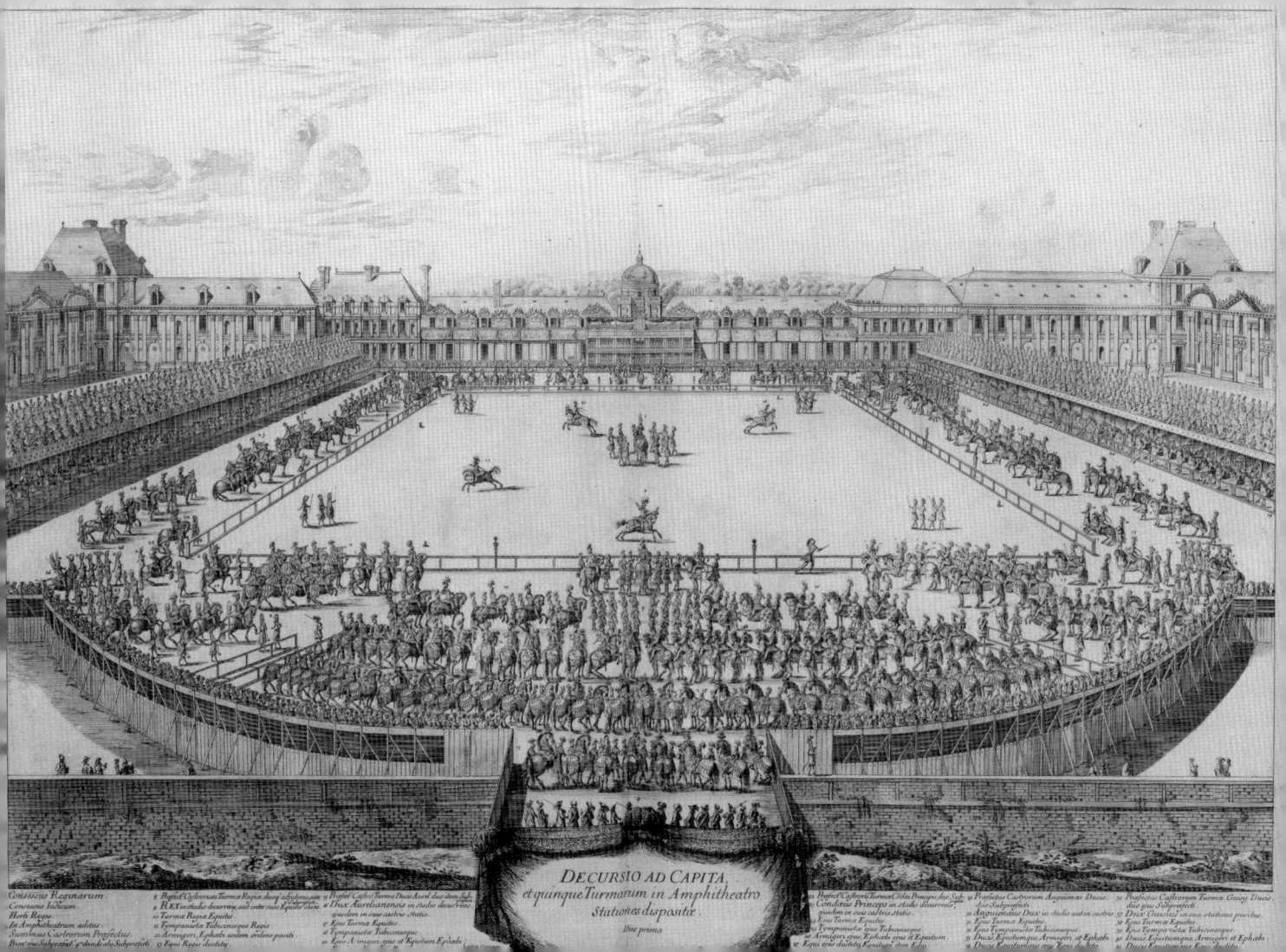

DECURSIO AD CAPITA, et quinque Turmarum in Amphitheatro Stationes dispositæ.

38

Ein wahres Probiertes und Pracktisches geschriebenen Feuerbuch

1607

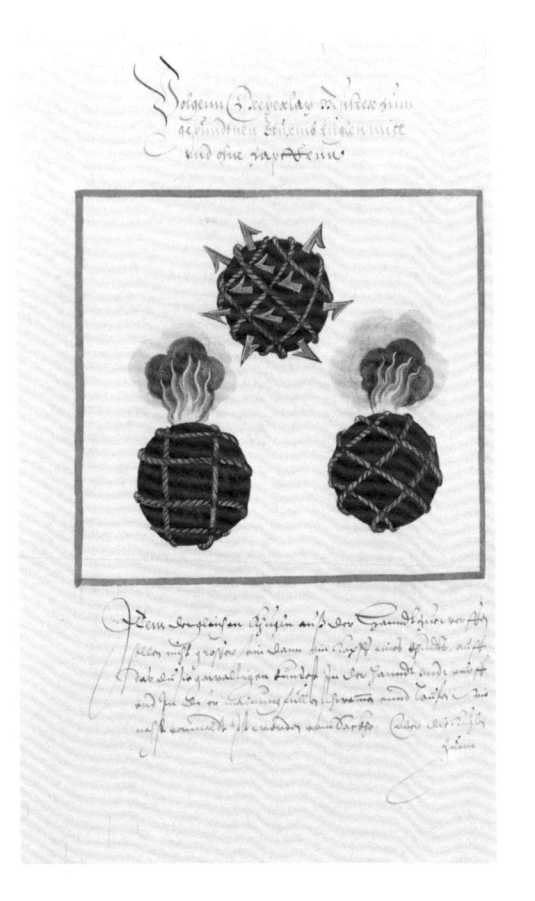

Treatises on fortification, artillery, and weaponry abounded in the major European languages in 16th- and 17th-century Europe. The need for besieging armies to penetrate castles and fortified towns made such manuals necessary. This elaborately illustrated German manuscript is one such manual. It is intended to be a practical guide on 17th-century incendiary devices, as well as a book of instruction for the master gunner or Buchsenmeister. It contains thirty contemporary hand-colored illustrations which depict the form, structure, and performance of rockets, cannonballs, and other explosive devices. One unique illustration shows the use of animals in besieging a town. A "jet-pack" cat and a pigeon are carrying explosives toward a beleaguered fortress. The second illustration exhibits the shape and the arming of an incendiary device. **RL**

Also das einem vom feur verwundt werden, und verwund
mit grosser macht unnd gewalt allerhand feurs werckh.

Ein Schloss durch ein Tauben zu͂ in zu erobern
darhin man sonst nit komen kann.

39

GEORG BRAUN AND FRANS HOGENBERG

Civitates orbis terrarum

Cologne, Petrum a Brachel, 1572

The *Civitates* is the first printed uniform collection of maps and plans of the main cities of the world. It is sometimes considered to be a companion piece to Ortelius's *Theatrum orbis terrarum* because of the similarity in title, format, layout, and the serial order of the maps and text. It was a collaborative effort by the engraver Frans Hogenberg, who worked on both projects simultaneously, and the priest Georg Braun. Braun edited the text, which includes the history, origin, place names, topography, principal places, government, and commerce of each city. The *Civitates* is notable because it demonstrates the various methods of depicting a town: the stereographic view, the bird's eye view, the linear ground view, and the map view which is a combination of the previous three views. The map of Paris is drawn from a bird's eye view and was copied from Sebastian Munster's *Cosmographia*. The map clearly follows the requirement that Braun sets forth in the foreword to Book II that "... towns should be drawn in such a manner that the viewer can look into all the roads and streets and see all the buildings and open spaces." The map of Ormuz (in Persia) was taken from a Portuguese manuscript and is drawn from a stereographic view. **RL**

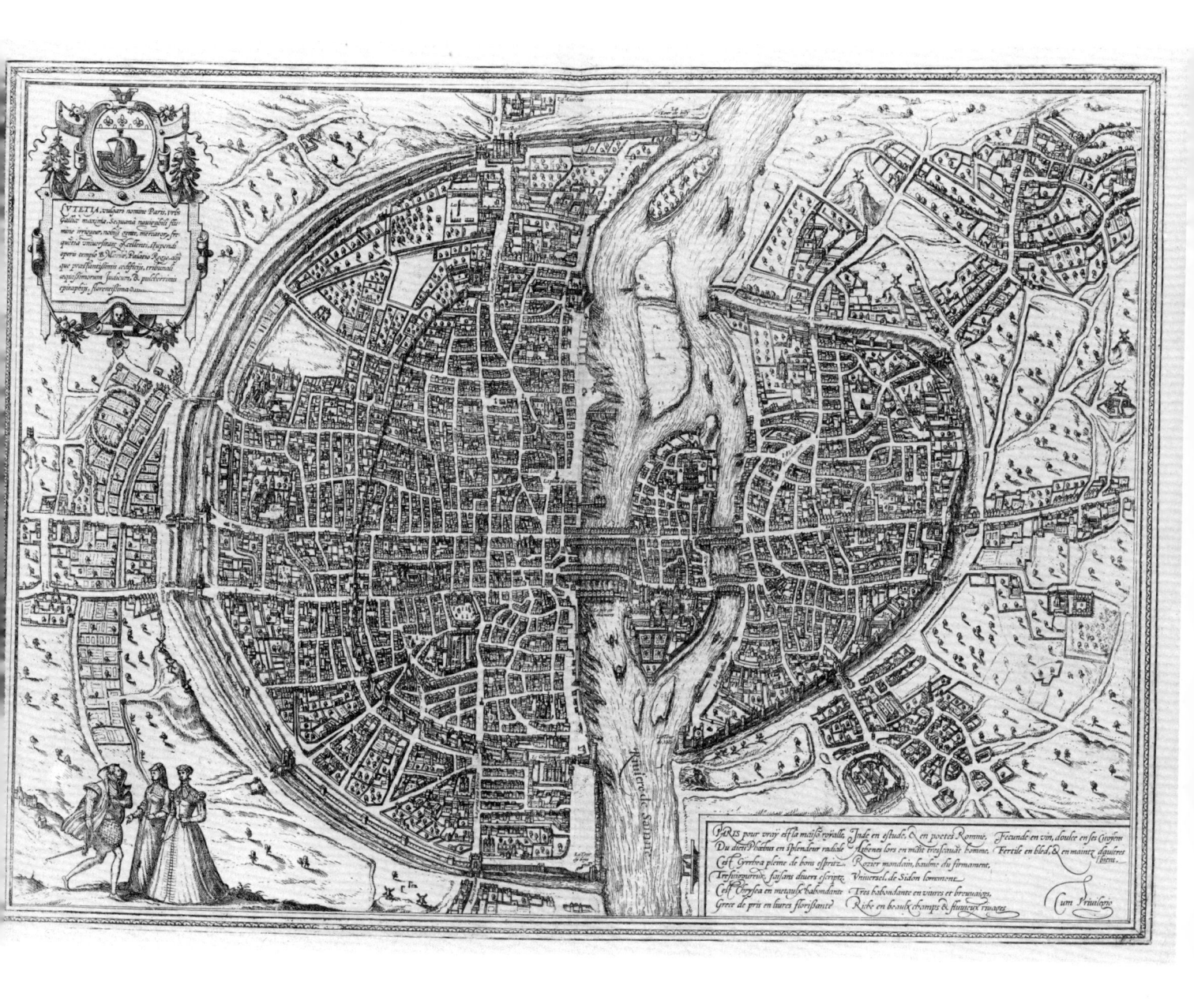

LVTETIA, vulgari nomine Paris, vrbs
Galliæ maxima, Sequana nauigabili flu-
mine irrigua, nouij cremj, mercatorq́; fre-
quentia vniuersitate celebris, stupendi
operis templo B. Mariæ, Palatio Regio, atq́;
que præstantissimis ædificijs, tribunali
æquissimorum iudicum, & pulcherrimo
episcopijs, florentissima ciuit.

PARIS pour vroy est la maiso royalle. Inde en estude, & en poetes Romme. Fecunde en vin, doulce en ses Citoyens
Du dieu Phœbus en splendeur radieuse Athenes lors en midit treschaude homme. Fertile en bled, & en maintz esquires lieux.
C'est Cerebra pleine de bons espritz Rozier mondain, baulme du firmament.
Tresinuquieux, faisans diuers escriptz Vniuersel, de Sidon lonenome.
C'est Chrysea en metaulx habondante Tres habondante en viures et brouuaiges.
Grece de pris en liures florissante Riche en beaulx champs & fluueux riuages.

Cum Priuilegio

HARTMANN SCHEDEL
Liber chronicarum
[Nuremberg, Anton Koberger, 12 July, 1493]

From 1487 to 1493, the energies of the Nuremberg book collector, scholar, and physician Hartmann Schedel were concentrated on researching and writing this Latin edition of the *Nuremberg Chronicle*. During part of this time, the artists Michael Wolgemut and Wilhelm Pleydenwurff were working on the beautiful woodcuts. They possibly had the assistance of the artist, Albrecht Dürer, who was then an apprentice in Wolgemut's workshop. The patrons, Sebolt Schreyer, a wealthy Nuremberg merchant, and his brother-in-law, Sebastian Kammermeister, contracted with the author and later with the artists to produce this illustrated history of the world from the Creation to 1493. The publishing and bookselling firm of Anton Koberger, the greatest and largest firm in Europe at that time, did the printing. The *Chronicle* is considered to be a remarkable book because of its graphic design and because, in 1493, it held the record for having the greatest number of illustrations in a printed book in Europe. It contains woodcut illustrations of biblical scenes, emperors, rulers, popes, as well as maps of cities and countries. There are a total of 1,809 woodcut illustrations made from 645 woodblocks. Many of the woodcuts were used repeatedly, for example, the 96 woodcuts of emperors, rulers, and popes were used 598 times and the 53 woodcuts of cities and countries were used to depict 101 different places. ***RL***

Folium VII

Cunq; suggerente diabolo in forma serpentis pthoparētes mandatuz dei trās/gressi fuissent: maledixit eis deus: et ait serpenti. Maledict9 eris inter omnia animātia τ bestias terre: super pectus tuum gradieris: et terram comedes cunctis diebus vite tue. Mulieri quoq; dixit. Mlitiplicabo erūnas tuas: τ cōceptus tuos: in dolore paries filios τ sb viri potestate eris: τ ipse dōiabitur tibi. Ade vo dixit Maledicta terra in opere tuo ī laboribus comedes ex ea: spinas τ tribulos germinabit tibi: in sudore vultus tui vesceris pane tuo: donec reuertaris in terram de qua sumptus es. Et cū feciss; eis deus tunicas pelliceas eiecit eos de paradiso collocans ante illum cherubin cum flammeo gladio: vt viam ligni vite custodiat.

Adam primus homo formatus de limo terre triginta annorū apparens imposito nomine Eua vxori sue. Cuz de fructu ligni vetiti oblato ab vxore sua comedisset: eiecti sunt de paradiso voluptat]: in terram maledictionis vt iuxta imprecationez domini dei. Adā in sudore vultus sui operaretur terram: et pane suo vesceretur. Eua quoq; in erūnis viueret filios quoq; pareret in dolore. quam imcompabili splendore decorauit. eā felicitatis sue inuid9 hostis decepit: cū leuitate feminea fructus arboris temerario ausu degustauit: τ virū suū in sentētiam suam traxit. Deinde perizomatibus folioru susceptis ex delitiaʒ orto in agro ebron vna cuz viro pulsa exul venit. Tandem cuz partus dolores sepius expta fuisset cuz laboribus in senū τ tande in mortez sibi a domino predictā deuenit.

41

WILLIAM SHAKESPEARE
Plays
London, J. Edwards, 1797

In 1797 a six-volume set of Shakespeare's works was printed by the Edwards firm of Halifax in England. The firm was noted for its beautifully bound books with painted "Etruscan" or calf-skin bindings and painted fore-edges. Although the technique of painting the fore-edge of a book may vary, several steps are necessary. The fore-edge pages of a book are fanned and then clamped tightly between wooden boards. A picture is then painted with water color. When the painting is dry, gilt is expertly applied so that it sticks to the edge without running into the painting. Thus the painting is concealed when the book is closed. If the gilt is not applied properly, the painting will show through. The painting here is of the bridge over the Avon at Stratford. Each of the other five volumes in the set has a different painting on the fore-edge. **_RL_**

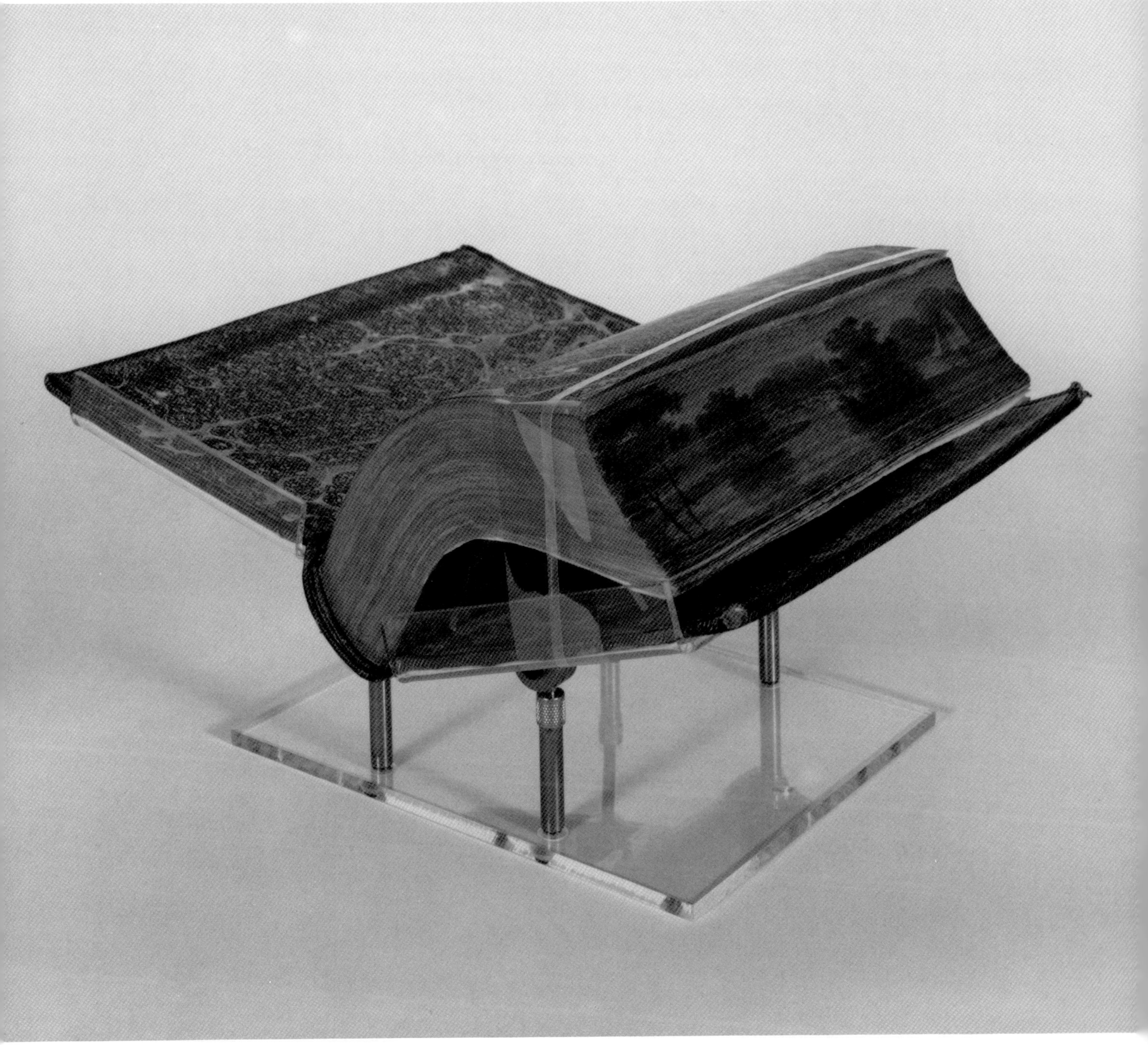

VINCENTINO LUDOVICO DEGLI ARRIGHI

La operina di Ludouico Vincentino, da imparare di scriuere littera cancellaresha

Venetia, 1533

Sixteenth-century Europe abounded with manuals on handwriting. Prominent among these manuals is *La Operina* or *Little Work*, first published in 1522 by the Italian writing master Ludovico Vincentino degli Arrighi. His work was the first book on the chancery cursive or italic hand, and also the first manual on handwriting that was printed in a handwritten script. The chancery cursive was made the official form of writing for all papal briefs in the Chancery office of the Catholic Church in the mid-15th century because of its beauty and its simplicity, and because it could be written faster than other scripts. Arrighi's instructions are simple yet informative. He teaches the student how the strokes of the letters should be written and how the letters should be shaped. Remarkable too is the typesetting by the woodblock cutter, Ugo da Carpi, who developed specifically for this manual the technique of cutting pages of cursive handwriting. *RL*

Vltra le retro-
scritte cinque littere a c d g q
ti fo intendere
che anchora quasi tutte le altre l're
se hanno á formare in questo :: qua=
dretto oblungo et non quadro per
fetto □
perche alocchio mio la littera
corsiua ouero Cancellarescha
vuole hauere
del
lungo & non del rotondo: che rotonda
ti veneria fatta quá=
do dal quadro
perfetto
& non oblungo la formasti

A IIII

MARTIN BILLINGSLEY

The pens excellencie or
The secretaries delight

[1618]

Martin Billingsley (1591-1622) has written in his manual that ". . . the Art of *Writing* is so excellent, and of such necessary use, that none ought to be without some knowledge therein. . . ." To be sure, handwriting was taken very seriously in Elizabethan and Jacobean England. *The pens excellencie* is one of the more influential writing manuals printed in England by an Englishman. In this, his first published work, Billingsley describes forms of handwriting that were prevalent in Europe and England in his day. He also discusses the secretary hand, or usual hand as it was often called. It was a very popular hand in England and was used in both governmental and private business. Although much in use in 1525, it was waning in influence by 1650, and had practically vanished by 1700. The title page of Billingsley's work shows both the secretary hand (the section beginning with "Wherein . . .") and the italic hand (the section beginning with "Together . . ."). **RL**

The Pens Excellencie

or

The Secretaries Delight

Wherein aswell the abuses wch are offered unto ye worthines of ye Pen, by unworthie Pen men, are trulie discovered: as ye Dignity of ye Art itselfe by ye Antiquitie, Excellencie & diversitie thereof, is briefly demonstrated

Together with an insertion of sondrie Peeces, or Examples, of all ye usuall Hands of England: as also an addition of certaine methodicall observations for Writing, Making of the Pen, Holding the Pen, &c.

Written by Martin Billingsley Mr in ye Art of Writing

Non satis est bene, aliquid facere, nisi etiam fiat venuste.   W: Hole sculp.

The Greeke & Hebrewe with other Peeces never yet extant are hereunto by the Authour exactlie added.

Are to be solde by Io: Sudbury & George Humble in Popeshead

44

JAN VAN DER HEYDEN

Beschryving der nieuwlijks witgevonden en geoctrojeerde slang-brand-spuiten. . . .

Amsterdam, Jan Rieuwertsz, 1690

This highly detailed engraving is one of many contained in this influential Dutch book on fire fighting and fire fighting equipment. Van der Heyden was a distinguished artist and a mechanical engineer and was the director of the municipal fire fighting department of Amsterdam for forty years. In 1690 he published this work on his inventions. The nineteen copperplate engravings show excellent depictions of buildings ablaze and the failure of the outdated fire system. Van der Heyden's invention of a new pump and a flexible canvas firehose advanced fire fighting by allowing firemen, using jet water, to get closer to the fire. His fire equipment became very popular not only in the Netherlands, but also in England. The ship that transported William and Mary to England after the abdication of James II in 1688, carried several of Van der Heyden's fire engines. ***RL***

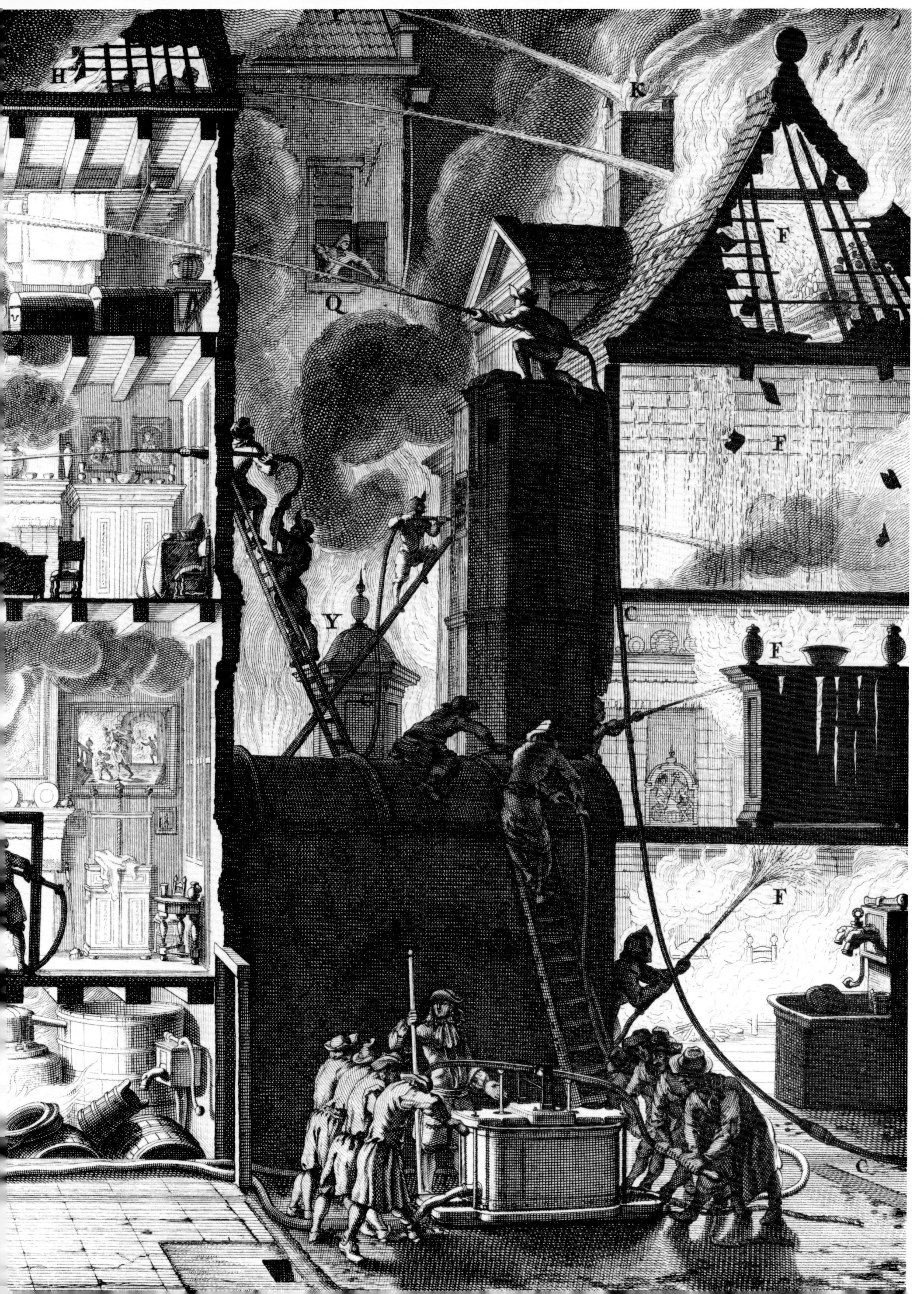
H
P
K
F
Q
F
Y
C
F
F
C

45

WILLIAM SHAKESPEARE

Songs and Sonnets by Shakespeare

1926

Alberto Sangorski spent almost three years creating this calligraphic masterpiece, one of the most beautifully designed and hand-crafted books of the 20th century. The calligraphy was done on the finest vellum using 23 karat gold leaf in the illuminations. Each page is interleaved with moire silk. The jeweled binding, also designed by Sangorski, has sapphires in the corners and Shakespeare's coat of arms in 18 karat gold, inlaid with a ruby in the center. Henry Clay Folger bought the book soon after it was finished. **JFM**

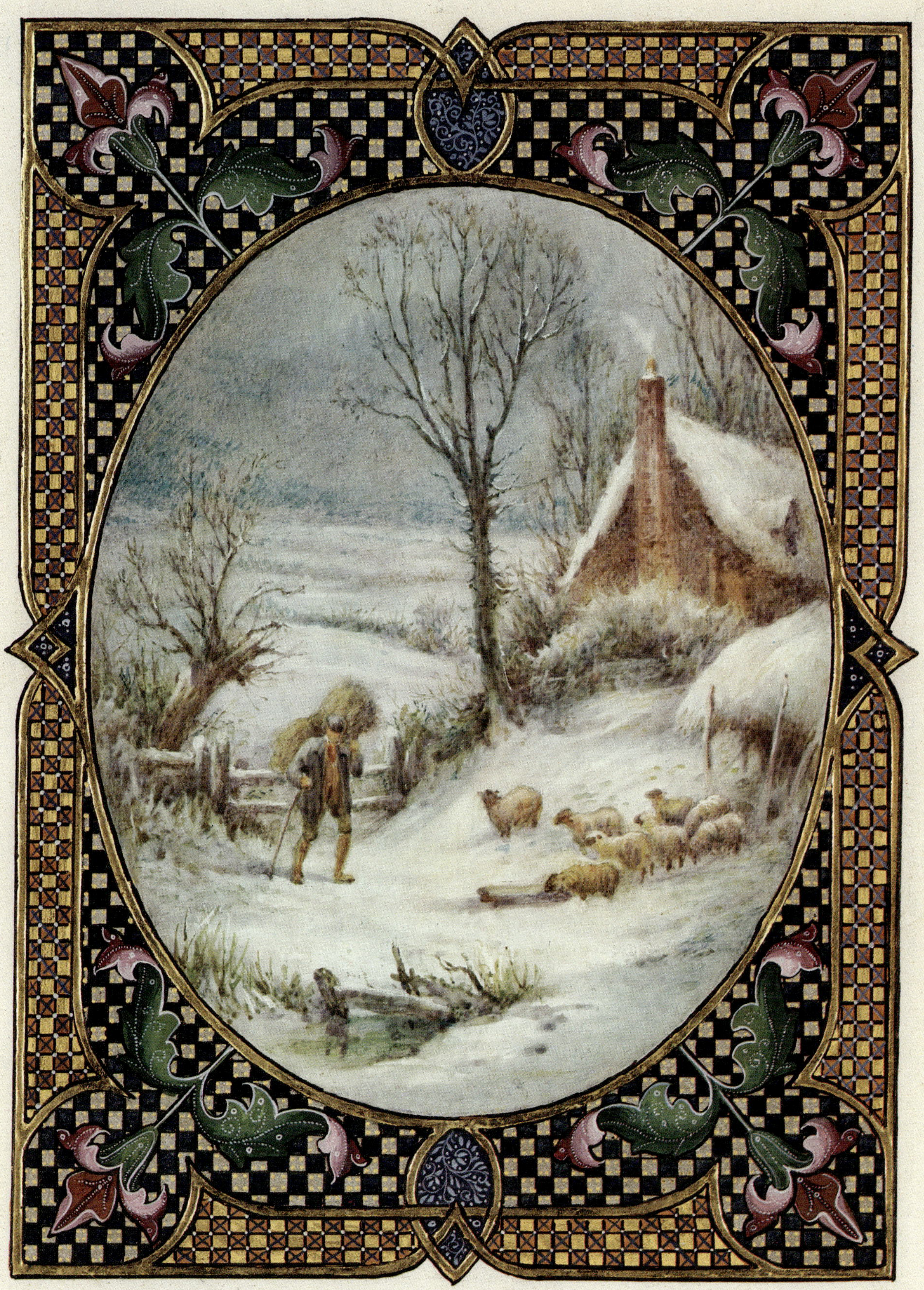

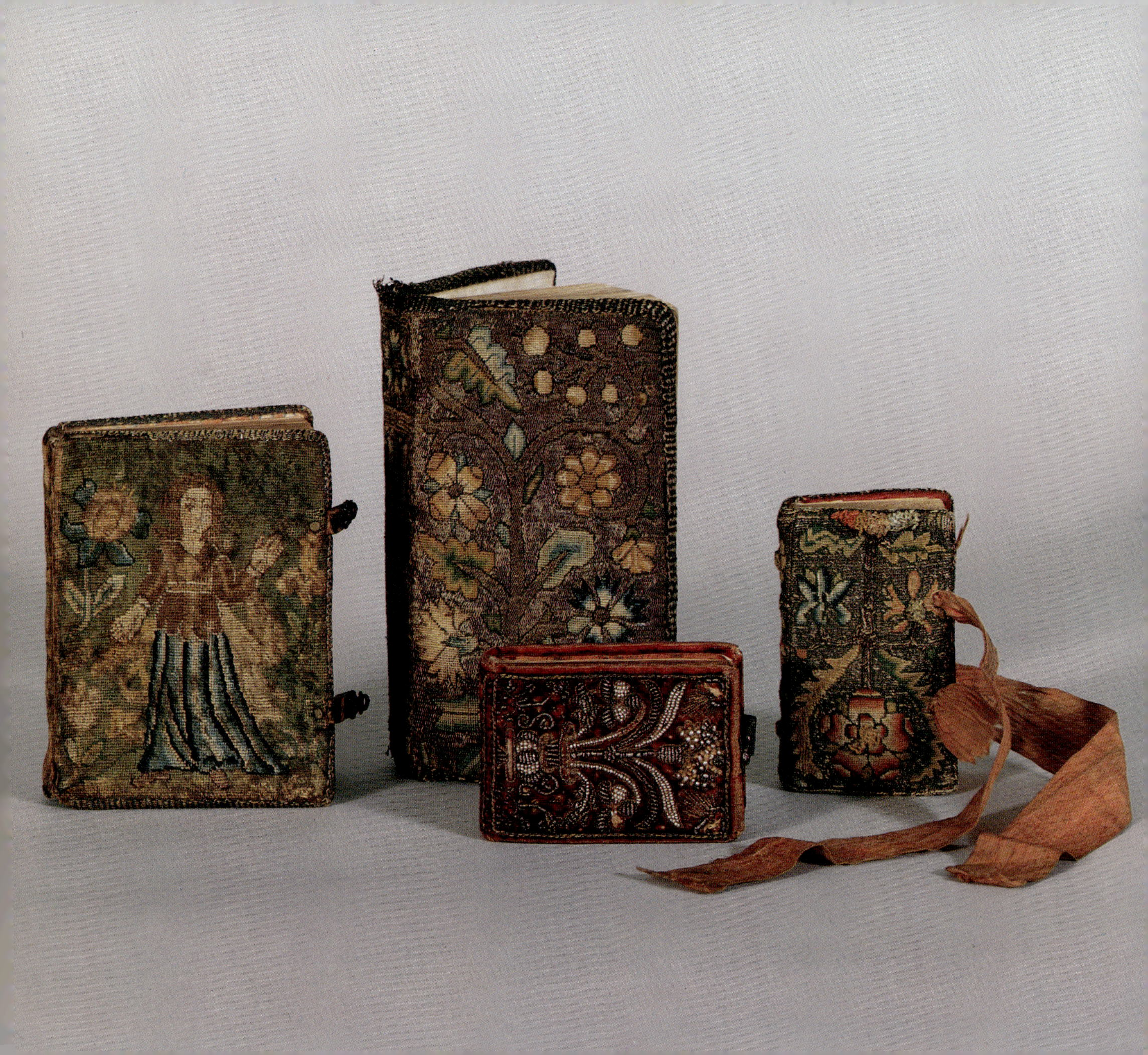

46
EMBROIDERED BINDINGS

The Whole Booke of Psalmes
London, 1635

The Whole Book of Davids Psalmes
London, T.C., 1635

THOMAS SOROCOLD
Supplications of Saints
London, I.D., 1630

ESTHER INGLIS
Argumenta Psalmorum
1608

These four volumes are just a few examples of the Folger Library's extraordinary collection of embroidered bindings. During the early part of the 17th century, it was fashionable for ladies to own embroidered devotional books. Some were probably embroidered by the owners themselves, but more than likely most were executed by professionals. These four examples show the diversity of design and technique. They are embroidered with silver, silk, and linen thread. One of the Folger's most prized bindings is the small red velvet manuscript written by Esther Inglis entitled *Argumenta Psalmorum*. It is decorated with raised silver thread and hundreds of seed pearls forming a floral arrangement stemming from a vase. The book is held closed by a beautiful silver clasp. ***JFM***

47

WILLIAM SHAKESPEARE

The Plays of Shakespeare

London, William Pickering, 1825

Charles S. Stratton, known as General Tom Thumb; 12 years old and 25 inches high; weighed 15 lbs.

This nine-volume set of Shakespeare's plays, printed in London in 1825, is one of the earliest examples of artificially grained cloth made to resemble morocco leather. Each volume measures only 3½ by 2 inches. This set once belonged to the famous 19th-century personality Charles Stratton, better known as General Tom Thumb. Stratton, who was born on January 4, 1838, stopped growing at the age of six months and remained two feet and one inch tall, weighing only fifteen pounds until his teens when he finally grew to three feet and four inches. P.T. Barnum promoted him to international stardom. He was such a famous figure that in 1863, when he married Lavinia Warren, another dwarf in P.T. Barnum's show, the New York newspapers carrying the event almost forgot to mention the then raging Civil War.

Tom Thumb's Shakespeare is just one example in the Library's collection of books once belonging to famous people including presidents, royalty, and famous actors.   ***JFM***

KING RICHARD III.
Re-enter BUCKINGHAM, and the rest.
ACT IV. SCENE I.
Before the Tower.

48

WILLIAM SHAKESPEARE

The whole contention betweene the two famous houses, Lancaster and York; Pericles, Prince of Tyre

London, [1619]

These two 1619 volumes were bound together in 1907 by the Club Bindery in New York in red goatskin leather with green goatskin onlays. The gilding was done by Leon Maillard, who had been invited by the Club Bindery in 1897 to come to this country from France. Maillard was considered to be the best finisher in his day, a finisher being the person who does the onlay work and the gilding on the binding. The gold tooling, which was done with 23 karat gold, and the leather onlay are virtually perfect. The Club Bindery was closed in 1909, and Maillard and his associates moved to Cleveland where they reopened as the Rowfant Bindery. However, the firm encountered financial problems, and Maillard was forced to sell electric carpet sweepers to earn a living. In 1921, Maillard took his life.

The texts within this volume are known as "Pavier Quartos," after Thomas Pavier, who along with William Jaggard published these and several other unauthorized versions of Shakespeare's plays. The first volume in this binding is considered to be a corrupt version from what we now know to be parts 2 and 3 of *Henry VI.* **JFM**

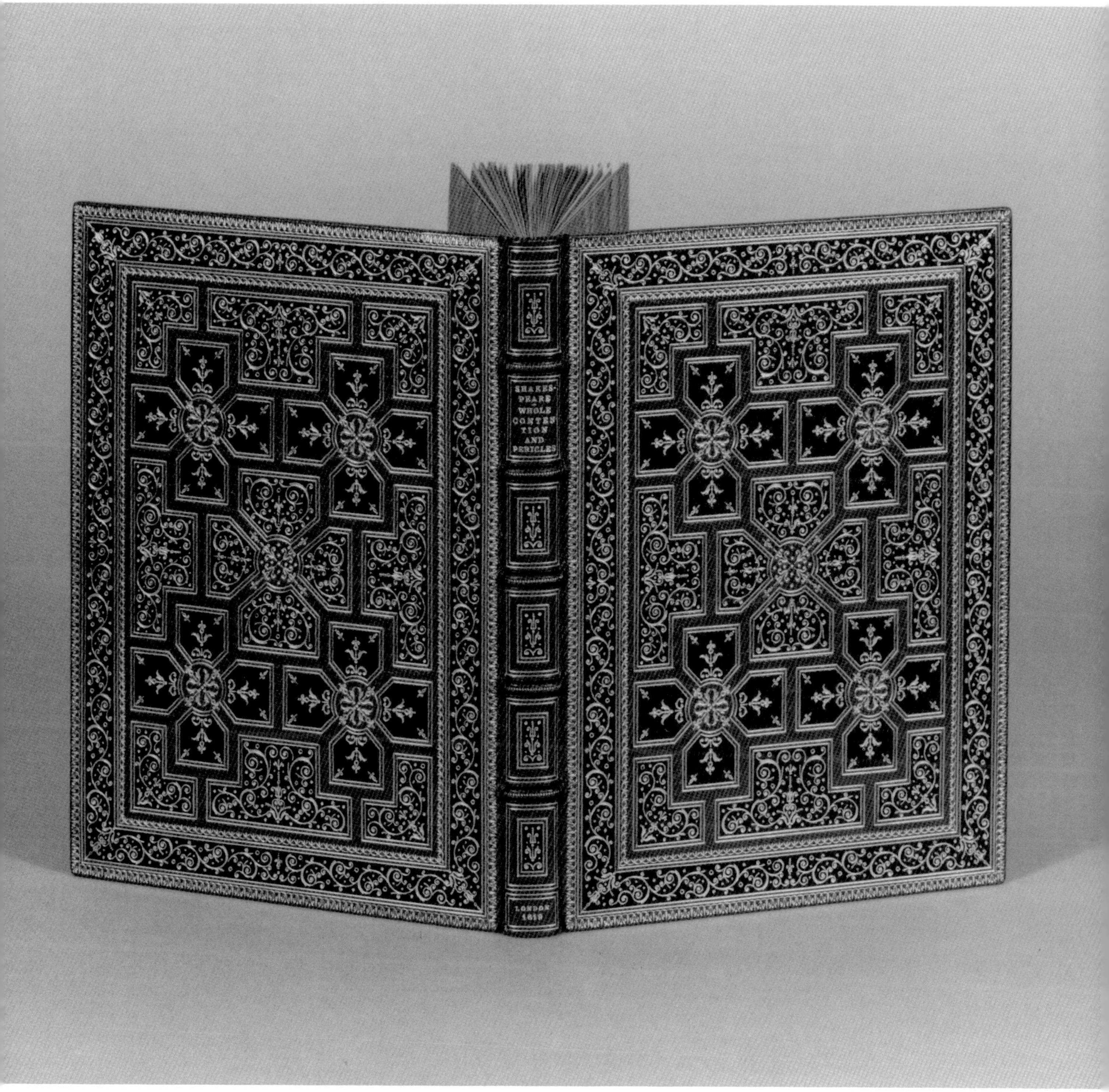
SHAKES-
PEARE
WHOLE
CONTEN
TION
AND
PERICLES
LONDON

ROYAL WARRANT OF JAMES THE FIRST

January 30, 1617

This original royal warrant with the great seal of James I is addressed to George More, Lieutenant of the Tower. It authorizes the release of Sir Walter Raleigh from the Tower of London on January 30, 1617. Sir Walter Raleigh is best known as the man who financed and masterminded the first colonization of Virginia. Raleigh's downfall began shortly after James I's accession to the throne when Raleigh was unjustly accused of involvement in a plot "to surprise the Kings person." The trial is a landmark in English constitutional history. On the day before he was to be executed, he was given a reprieve and imprisoned in the Tower of London. There he remained a prisoner from 1603 to 1617 during which time he wrote his monumental *History of the World*. With this warrant King James authorized Raleigh's release based upon the promise that Raleigh would undertake another voyage to the New World and bring back half a ton of gold ore for the crown in exchange for his liberty. The voyage was unfortunate from the start. Storms scattered the fleet, sinking and disabling many ships. They were driven by a hurricane, then caught in the doldrums for forty days. Short of water and prey to scurvy and fever, many of his crew members died. Finally landing in Guiana (now Venezuela), they set off in search of a Spanish gold mine. The attempt to win the mine ended in disaster, including the death of Raleigh's own son. Raleigh honorably returned to England to imprisonment in the Tower; his earlier order of execution was reinstated. He was beheaded October 29, 1618. As Sir Walter Raleigh lay his head on the block someone objected that he ought to be facing east. "What matter," he answered, "how the head lie, so the heart be right?"

JFM

[Royal warrant, heavily faded. Partially legible text follows:]

James by the grace of God King of England Scotland ffrance and Ireland defender of the faith &c. To our trusty [...] beloved Sir George Moore knight our Lieutenant of our Tower of London Greeting. Whereas [...] Sir Walter Raleigh knight having been heretofore by order of our late [...] convicted and attainted of high treason, by [...] of us and our Crowne which time through our pincely [...] forbearing to execute upon him [...] notwithstanding remained our prisoner in our said Tower. Where he still remaineth no [...] of you our Lieutenant there [...] signified under our signet to you our said Lieutenant [...] directed we commanded you to suffer the said Sir Walter Raleigh to goe abroad with his [...] City of London or elsewhere. Whereas accordingly you have done as wee are informed. And whereas we [...] ourselves of our [...] by these presents [...] out of our princely commiseration being graciously pleased that the said [...] shall be no longer continued prisoner in our said Tower, but forthwith be fully [...] enlarged and delivered out of the same, in hope he will [...] hereafter demeane himselfe to us and our State. Wee therefore will and require you our said Lieutenant of our said Tower immediately upon the receipt of these presents fully and wholly to enlarge and sett out of our said Tower the said Sir Walter Raleigh. The aforesaid [...] condemnation, or judgment given and passed against him, or any commandment, order or direction [...] Councell, or otherwise touching the same, to the contrary whereof in any wise notwithstanding. And these presents shall be your sufficient warrant and discharge in this behalfe. In witness whereof wee have caused these our letters to be made patents. Witnes our self at Westminster the thirtieth day of January in the fourteenth yeere of our Raigne of England ffrance and Ireland and of Scotland the fiftith.

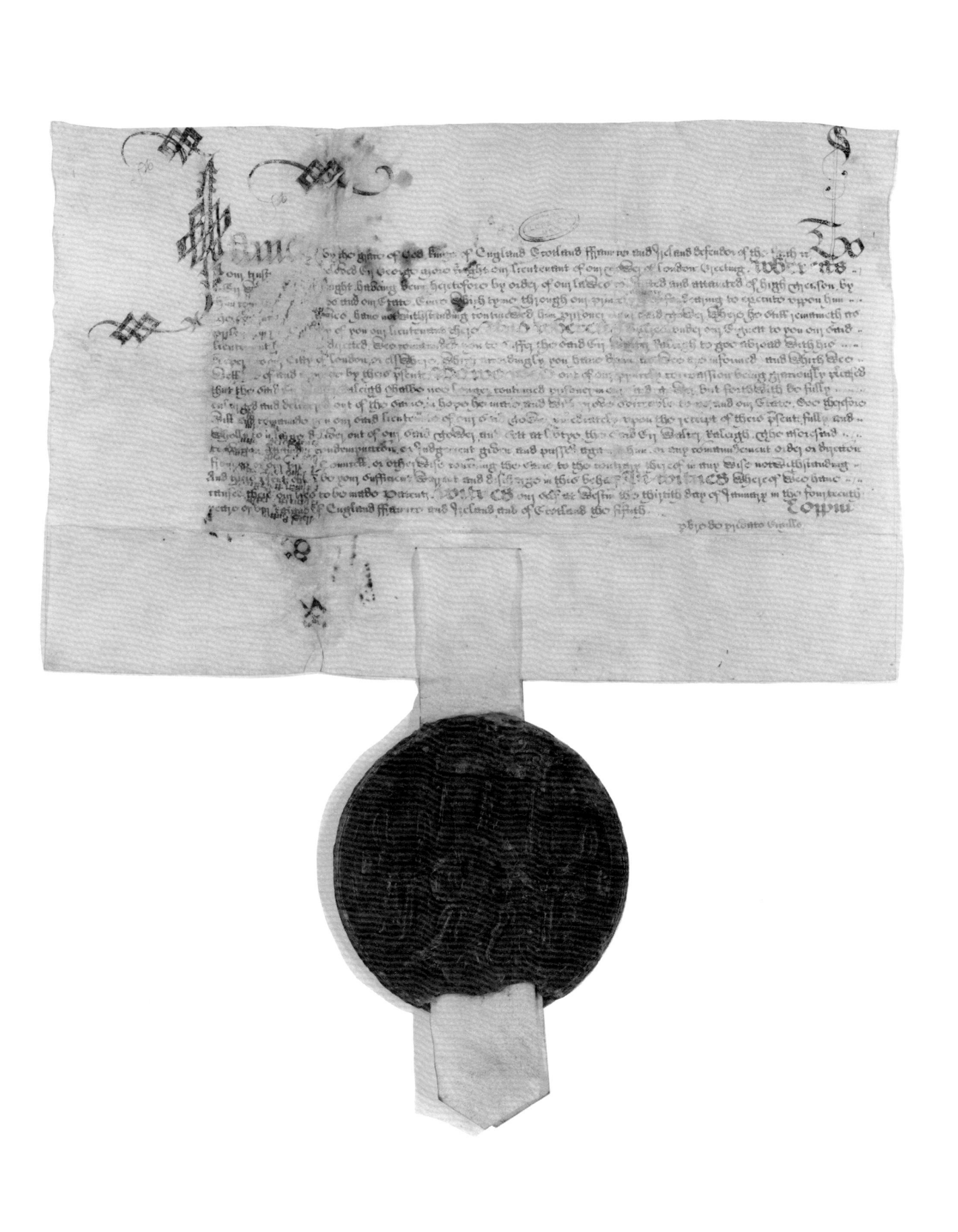

per breve de privato sigillo

WILLIAM WETMORE STOREY
"Seated William Shakespeare"
Marble Sculpture

Rome, 1879

This delicately carved marble figure of Shakespeare portrays the writer as a young man. It has the sculptor's monogram and ROMA 1879 carved under the left-hand side of the chair. Henry Clay Folger purchased this sculpture from Henry Kirschenbaum in 1928 for $300. William Storey was an American artist who lived from 1815 to 1895. After graduating from Harvard he decided to pursue a career as an artist. He traveled to Italy where he studied and worked for many years. Shakespeare's pose is similar to Storey's most famous sculpture, the seated bronze figure of Justice John Marshall located in front of the U.S. Capitol. ***JFM***

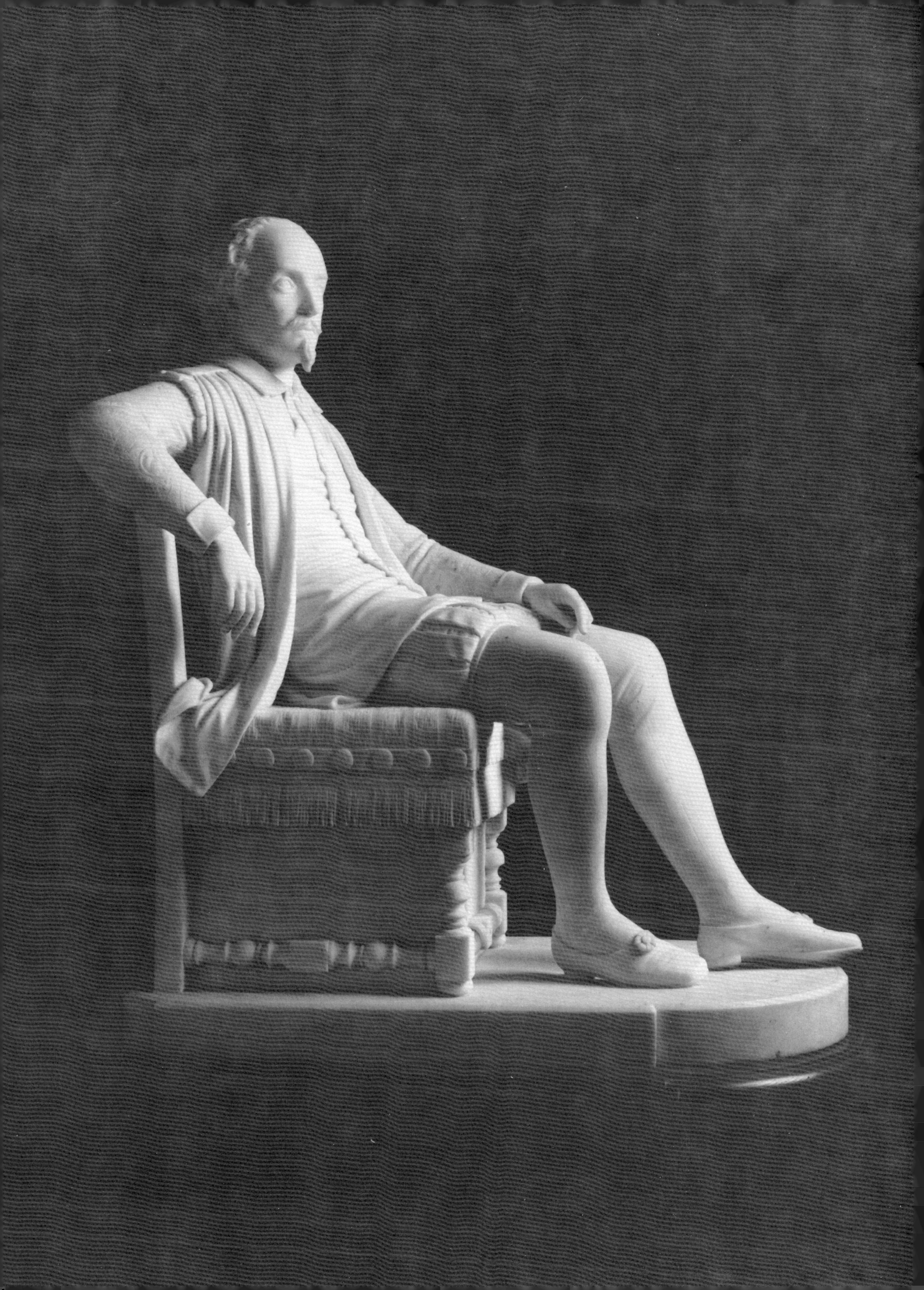

HORNBOOK

The A.B.C. with the Lord's Prayer . . .

[London?, ca. 1625]

The Elizabethan child's first introduction to formal education began with his entrance into petty school at the age of four. There he learned his letters with the assistance of a simple tablet called a hornbook. A hornbook is a piece of wood on which is mounted a leaf of paper containing the alphabet, some elements of spelling, and the Lord's Prayer, usually printed in black letter (gothic type). The paper was covered with a thin piece of translucent horn held in place by strips of brass, thus giving the book its name. This hornbook is covered in leather and has stamped on the back an impression of Saint George slaying the dragon. Hornbooks were generally used from the 15th through the 18th centuries. Young William Shakespeare probably learned his ABCs from a hand held hornbook such as this. *JFM*

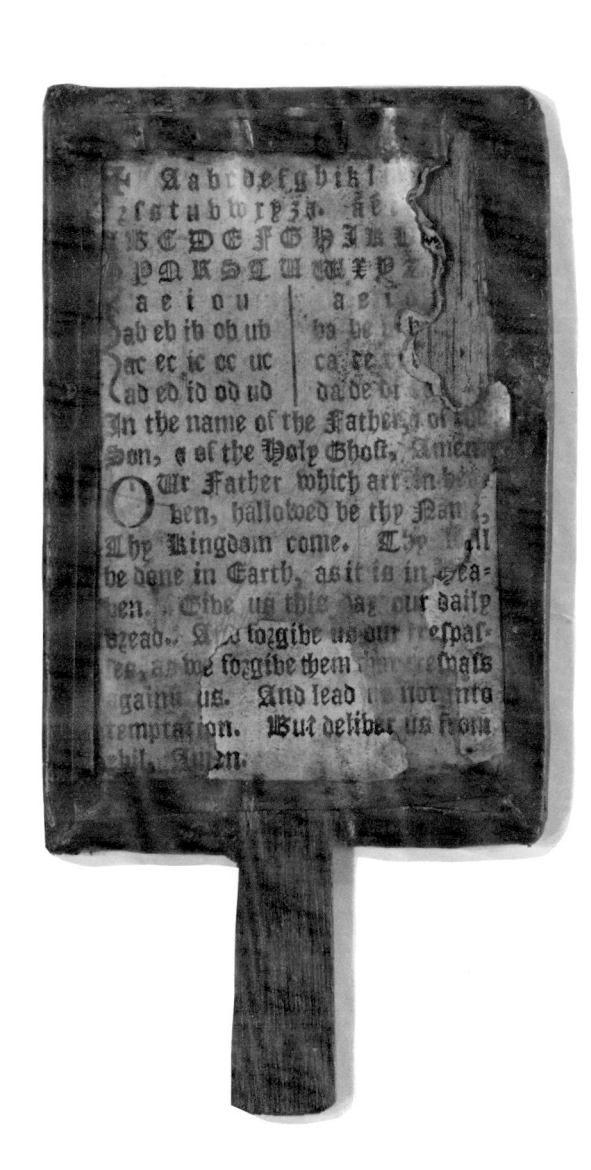

A a b c d e f g h i j k l
m n o p q r s t u v w x y z.   &
A B C D E F G H I K L M N O
P Q R S T U W X Y Z

a e i o u   a e i o u
ab eb ib ob ub   ba be bi bo bu
ac ec ic oc uc   ca ce ci co cu
ad ed id od ud   da de di do du

In the name of the Father, & of the
Son, & of the Holy Ghost, Amen.

Our Father which art in heaven, hallowed be thy Name.
Thy Kingdom come. Thy will
be done in Earth, as it is in Heaven. Give us this day our daily
bread. And forgive us our trespasses, as we forgive them that trespass
against us. And lead us not into
temptation. But deliver us from
evil. Amen.

MATTHEW PARKER
A Defence of Priestes Mariages
London, 1567?

This exquisite contemporary brown calf binding has painted decorations. It was probably bound around 1570 by the MacDurnan Gospels Binder, Archbishop Parker's private binder for the last five years of his life. Over thirty bindings are known to have been produced by this bindery, this one being a recently discovered example. Characteristic of these bindings are the cornucopia corners, centerpieces, and an obliquely hatched opening-bud found above and below the centerpiece. This style is closely copied from French bindings but the ornamentation of the spine and the gauffered edges of the leaves are characteristically English.

Matthew Parker studied at Cambridge and was appointed chaplain to Anne Boleyn, the second wife of Henry VIII. Parker later became the chaplain to the King himself. On the accession of Mary to the throne, he fell out of favor with the authorities; the fact of his marriage to Margaret Harlestone in 1547 alone supplied sufficient grounds to deprive him of all promotions. Throughout Mary's reign he lived in obscurity and continuous fear of being discovered. On the accession of Elizabeth, Parker regained his previous stature in the Church and in 1559, was installed as Archbishop of Canterbury. Queen Elizabeth was opposed to clerics' marriages, but during a visit to Parker's residence, Lambeth Palace, she was touched by the grace and courtesy of her reception. Unable to suppress her dislike for clerical marriages, however, she took leave of her hostess with the oft-quoted words, "Madam, I may not call you; Mistress, I am ashamed to call you; But yet I thank you."
JFM

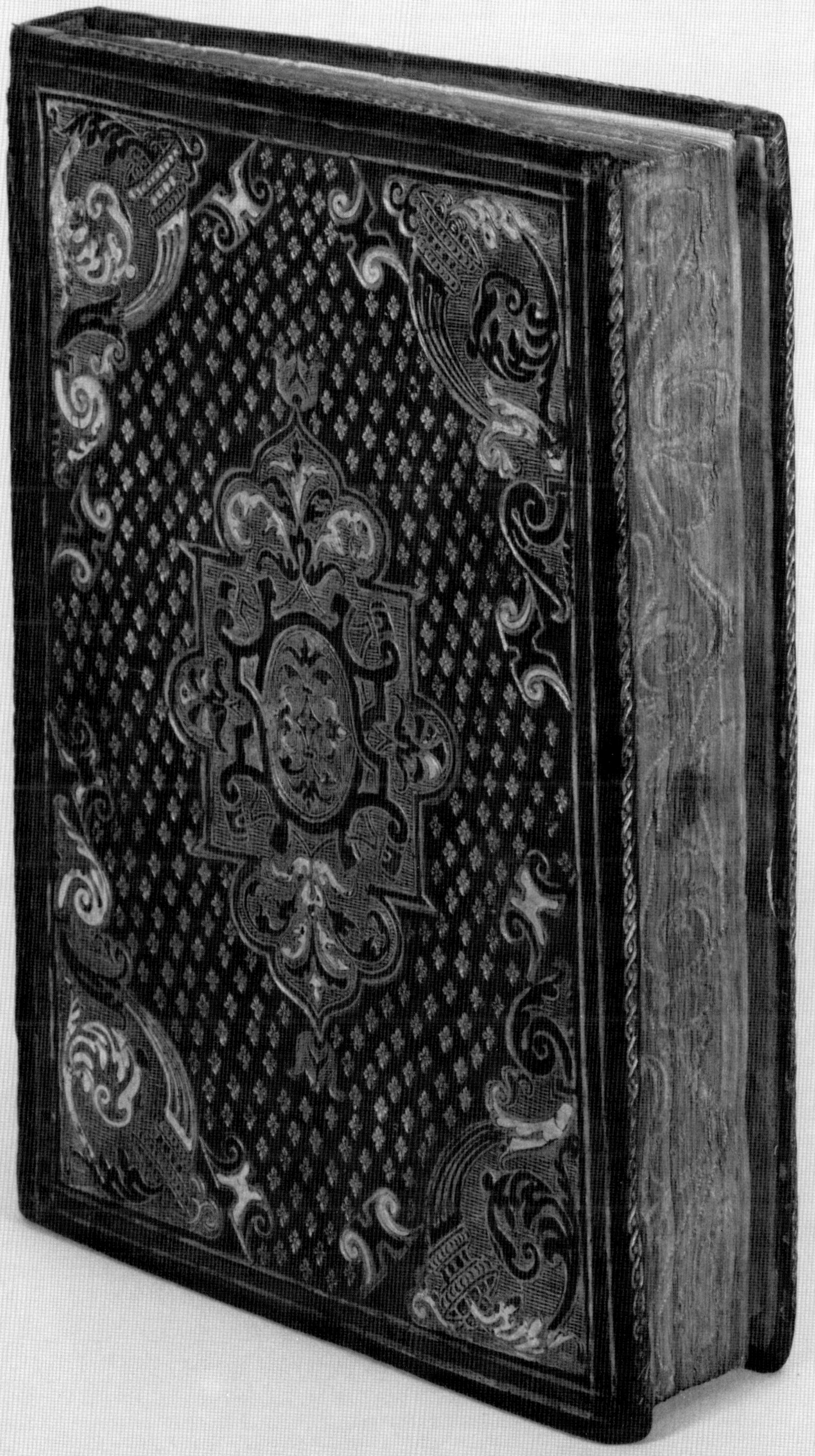

THOMAS À KEMPIS

Opera et libri vite fratris thome de kempis. . . .

[Nuremberg, Caspar Hochfelder, Nov. 29, 1494]

This volume, one of a very few existing examples of a chain binding, still retains the remnant of the hand wrought chain which fastened it securely to a shelf. At the time of the publication of this book in the 1490s, books were considered extremely valuable possessions, and thus had to be guarded carefully.

This book by Thomas à Kempis, the Augustinian canon whose work the *Imitation of Christ* was widely translated, contains two works, and is bound in pigskin over shaped wooden boards and embellished with protective brass clasps and bosses. An inscription appears on the front cover protected by a thin piece of transparent horn mounted in a brass frame. **JFM**

Thomas de
kempis ser-
mones ab fr̄s

54

GEORGE TURBERVILLE
The noble art of venerie, or hunting
London, Christopher Barker, 1575

This binding is probably a 19th-century creation, covered in real deerskin fur and embellished with sterling silver bosses of running stags and Tudor roses. On the inside of the covers the doubleurs and flyleaves are leather, stenciled to depict a running hare and a fox. Printed by Christopher Barker at the "signe of the Grashopper in St Paules Churchyard," it is illustrated with many woodcuts showing various hunting scenes. This work was the second publication of this English poet, who also wrote *The booke of faulconrie or hauking*, which is often found bound with *The noble art of venerie, or hunting*. **JFM**

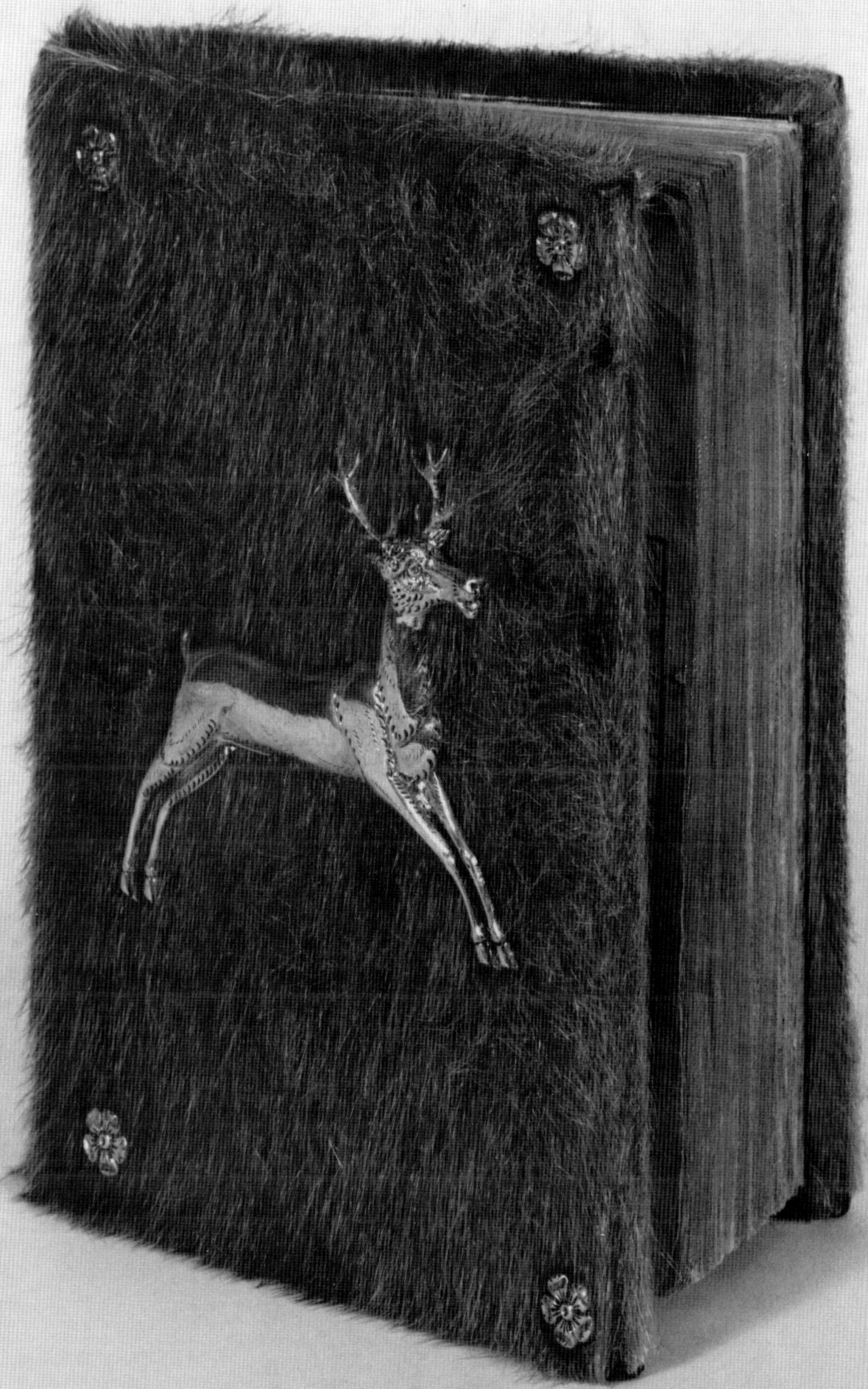

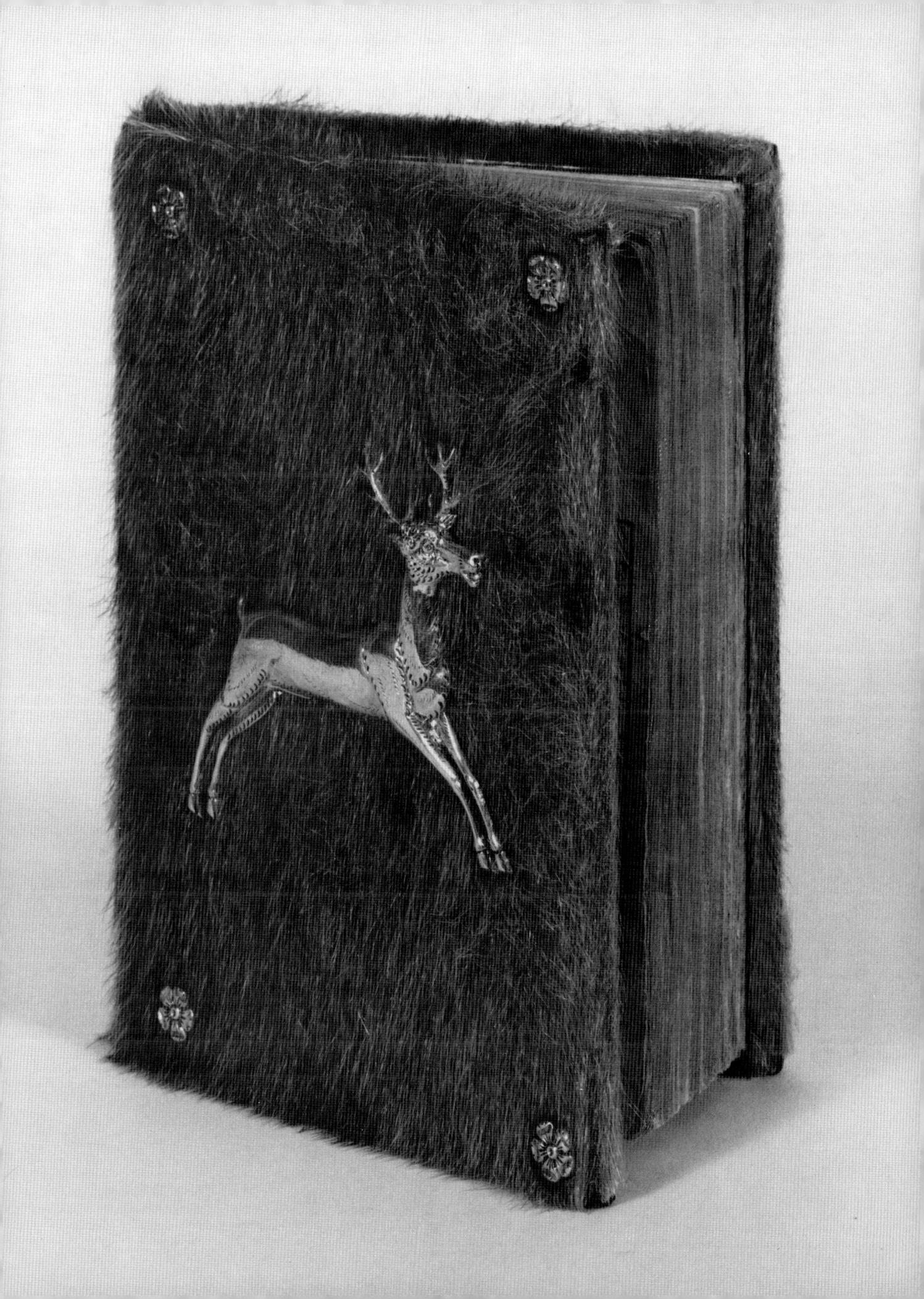

55

FLEMISH ALLEGORICAL TAPESTRY

Early 16th Century

This tapestry is one of several in the Folger collection. The figure seated in the center holding an orb and a sceptre is flanked on the right by a winged figure and on the left by a standing figure in armor, both helping to support the orb. The figures, symbolic of Wisdom, Justice, and Mercy, are all on a dais with blossoming plants in the foreground. The plants depicted were commonly used in the medical treatment of women. Woven in shades of blue, green, red and brown, the recently restored tapestry measures 8' 3" x 8' 5½". ***JFM***

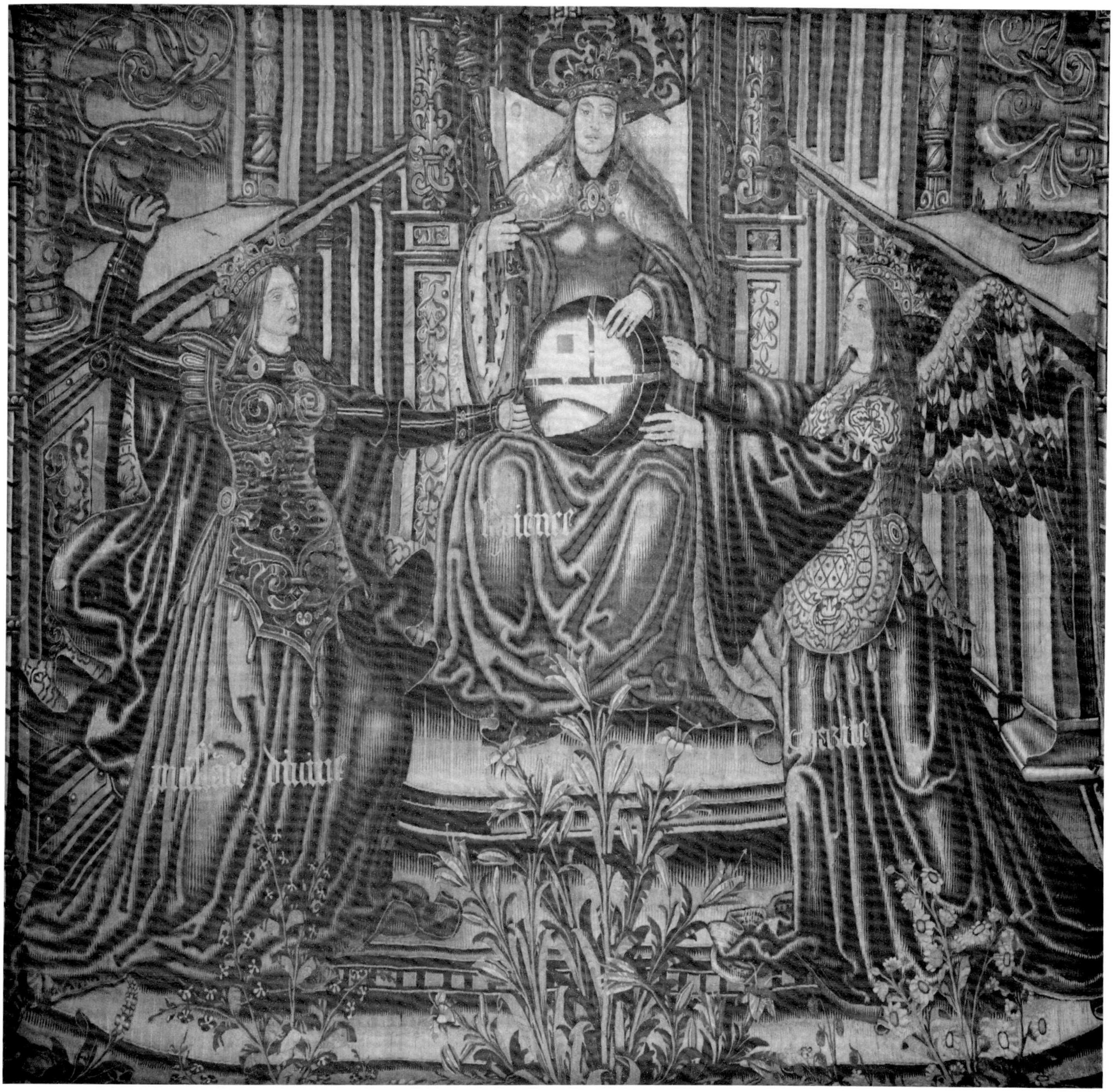

OBJECTS IN THE EXHIBITION

23
ARIOSTO, LUDOVICO. *Orlando Furioso.* Venice, Giolito de Ferrari, 1544.

42
ARRIGHI, VINCENTINO LUDOVICO DEGLI. *La operina di Ludouico Vincentino, da imparare di scriuere littera cancellaresha.* Venetia, 1533.

20
BELON, PIERRE. *L'Histoire de la nature des oyseaux.* Paris, Benoist Preuost, 1555.

22
BIBLIA GERMANICA. Nuremberg, Anton Koberger, 17 Feb. 1483.

43
BILLINGSLEY, MARTIN. The pens excellencie or The secretaries delight. [1618].

28
BOCCACCIO, GIOVANNI. *Il Decamerone.* Venice, Giolito de Ferrari, 1552.

12
BOCK, HIERONYMUS. *Hieronymi Tragi, De Stirpium.* . . . Argentorati, Wendelinus Rihelius, 1552.

39
BRAUN, GEORG, AND FRANS HOGENBERG. *Civitates orbis terrarum.* Cologne, Petrum a Brachel, 1572.

24
CALVIN, JOHN. *Institutio Christianae Religionis* together with the same author's *Harmonia ex tribus Evangelistis composita.* Geneva, Robert Stephanus, 1559–1560.

30
CERVANTES SAAVEDRA, MIGUEL DE. *El Ingenioso Hidalgo Don Quixote de la Mancha.* Brussels, Roger Velpius and Huberto Antonio, 1611.

17
CHAUCER, GEOFFREY. *The Canterbury Tales.* London, William Caxton, ca. 1478.

8
CICERO, MARCUS TULLIUS. *Commentū familiare in Ciceronis officia.* [Lyons, 1502].

13
DIDEROT, DENIS, ED. *Encyclopédie.* Paris, Briasson, 1751–65.

9
DONNE, JOHN. Letter to Sir George More. March 1602.

36
DOWLAND, JOHN. *The first booke of songes and ayres of fowre partes with tableture for the lute.* . . . [London], Peter Short, 1597.

7
ELIZABETH I. Letter to Henry IV of France. ca. 1595.

27
ERASMUS, DESIDERIUS. *Moriae Encomium,* or *Stultitiae Laus.* Basel, Iohannes Froben, 1519.

55
FLEMISH ALLEGORICAL TAPESTRY. Early 16th Century.

51
HORNBOOK. *The A.B.C. with the Lord's Prayer.* . . . [London?, ca. 1625].

10
Incipiunt hore beate marie virginis secudum usum sarum. Paris, [Philippe Pigouchet], 1497.

47
INGLIS, ESTHER. *Argumenta Psalmorum.* 1608.

34
INGLIS, ESTHER. *Octonaries upon the vanity and inconstancy of the world.* Dec. 23, 1607.

2
Kalendrier des bergers. [London, Thomas Este, 1570?].

21
LAMB, CHARLES. *The Midsummer Night's Dream.* London, M.J. Godwin, 1811.

31
LE ROY, LOUIS. *De la vicissitude ou variete des choses en l'univers, et concurrence des armes et des lettres par les premieres et plus illustres nations du monde, depuis le temps où à commencé la civilité iusques À present.* Paris, Pierre l'Huilier, 1575.

25
LUTHER, MARTIN. *Ad Leonem X Pontificem Maximum Resolutiones disputationum de virtute indulgentiarum.* Wittenberg, October, 1518.

33
MACHIAVELLI, NICCOLO. *Il Principe de Niccholo Machiavello al Magnifico Lorenzo di Piero de Medici.* Rome, Antonio Blado d'Asolo, January 4, 1532.

21
MENDELSSOHN, FELIX BARTHOLDY. *Overture to Shakespeare's Midsummernight's dream arranged as a duet for two performers on piano.* 10 July [1826?].

1
MILTON, JOHN. *Areopagitica: a speech of Mr. John Milton for the liberty of unlicenc'd printing.* London, 1644.

29
MONTAIGNE, MICHEL EYQUEM DE. *Les Essais.* Paris, Abel l'Angelier, 1598.

32
MORE, THOMAS. *De optimo reip. statu, deque nova insula Utopia, libellus vere aureus.* . . . Basel, Iohannes Froben, December, 1518.

35
ORTELIUS, ABRAHAM. *The theatre of the whole world.* . . . London, Iohn Norton, 1606.

14
PALLADIO, ANDREA. *I quattro libri dell'architetture.* . . . Venetia, Bartolomeo Carampello, 1581.

52
PARKER, MATTHEW. *A Defence of Priestes Mariages.* London, 1567?

37
PERRAULT, CHARLES. *Festiva ad capita annulumque decursio, a rege Ludovico XIV.* . . . Parisiis, E typographia regia, 1670.

26
PETRARCA, FRANCESCO. *Il Petrarcha: Con l'espositione d'Allessandro Vellutello di novo ristampato con le figure a i triomphi, et con piu cose utili in varii luoghi aggiunte.* Venice, Giolito de Ferrari, 1545.

21
RACKHAM, ARTHUR. "Are you sure that we are awake. . . ?" London, William Heinmann, 1908.

15
REMMELIN, JOHANN. *Catoptrum Microcosmicum.* . . . Frankfurt am Main, Anton Hummen, 1660.

18
REPLICA OF SHAKESPEARE'S TEMPLE AT GARRICK'S HOME. ca. 1830.

49
ROYAL WARRANT OF JAMES THE FIRST. January 30, 1617.

40
SCHEDEL, HARTMANN. *Liber chronicarum.* [Nuremberg, Anton Koberger, 12 July, 1493].

3
SHAKESPEARE, WILLIAM. *Mr. William Shakespeares comedies, histories and tragedies.* London, Isaac Jaggard and Ed. Blount, 1623.

4
SHAKESPEARE, WILLIAM. *Mr. William Shakespeares comedies, histories and tragedies.* London, Thos. Cotes, 1632.

5
SHAKESPEARE, WILLIAM. *Mr. William Shakespeares comedies, histories and tragedies.* London, 1664.

6
SHAKESPEARE, WILLIAM. *Mr. William Shakespeares comedies, histories and tragedies.* London, 1685.

41
SHAKESPEARE, WILLIAM. *Plays.* London, J. Edwards, 1797.

47
SHAKESPEARE, WILLIAM. *The Plays of Shakespeare.* London, William Pickering, 1825.

45
SHAKESPEARE, WILLIAM. *Songs and Sonnets by Shakespeare.* 1926.

48
SHAKESPEARE, WILLIAM. *The whole contention betweene the two famous houses, Lancaster and York; Pericles, Prince of Tyre.* London, [1619].

19
SIXTEENTH-CENTURY LUTE.

46
SOROCOLD, THOMAS. *Supplications of Saints.* London, I.D., 1630.

50
STOREY, WILLIAM WETMORE. "Seated William Shakespeare." Marble Sculpture. Rome, 1879.

53
THOMAS À KEMPIS. *Opera et libri vite fratris thome de kempis.* . . . [Nuremberg, Caspar Hochfelder, Nov. 29, 1494].

11
TOPSELL, EDWARD. *The Historie of Foore-Footed Beastes.* London, William Iaggard, 1607.

54
TURBERVILLE, GEORGE. *The noble art of venerie, or hunting.* London, Christopher Barker, 1575.

44
VAN DER HEYDEN, JAN. *Beschryving der nieuwlijks witgevonden en geoctrojeerde slang-brand-spuiten.* . . . Amsterdam, Jan Rieuwertsz, 1690.

16
VISSCHER, CLAES JANSZ. *Londinum Florentissma Britanniae Urbs.* [ca. 1625].

38
Ein wahres Probiertes und Pracktisches geschriebenen Feuerbuch. 1607.

46
The Whole Booke of Davids Psalms. London, T.C. 1635.

46
The Whole Booke of Psalmes. London, 1635.

Colophon

Folger's Choice:
Favorites On Our Fifty-Fifth Anniversary

Designed by Hausmann/Krohn
Composed by Barbara Shaw
Display type is ITC Cheltenham
*Printed by Hagerstown Bookbinding
and Printing Company*